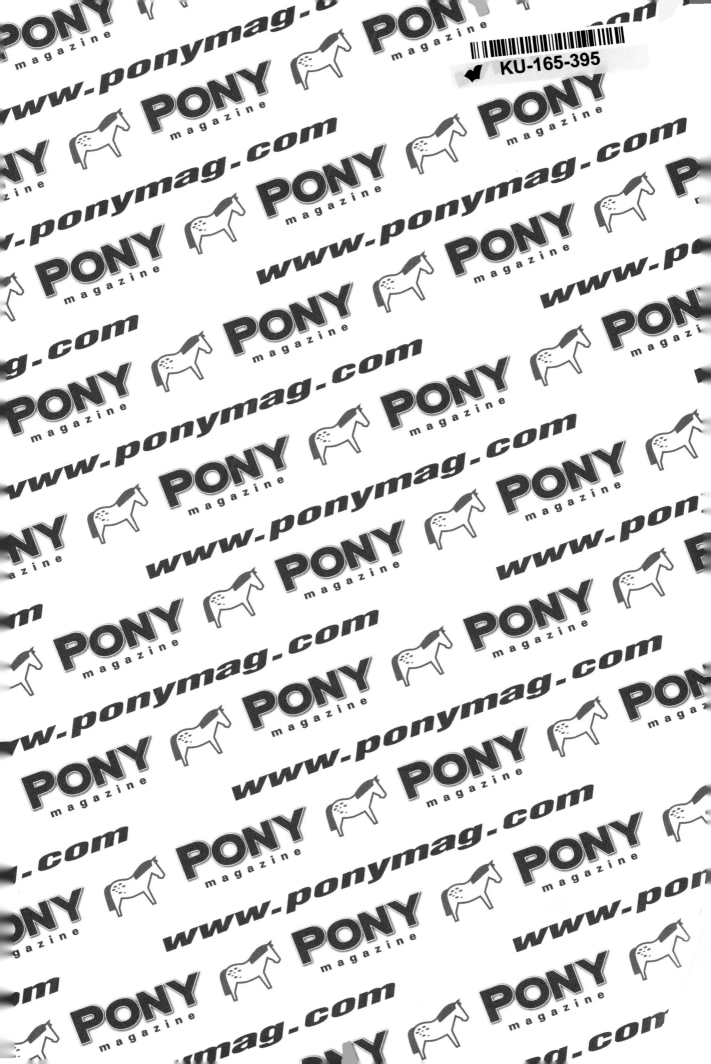

PONY: the annual!

First published in Great Britain in 2013
D J Murphy (Publishers) Ltd

ISBN-978-0-9556298-9-1

Who did what in **PONY: the annual!**

Editorial Team: **Janet Rising, Penny Rendall, Lucy King**
Art editor: **Paul Smail**
Published by: **D J Murphy (Publishers) Ltd**, Marlborough House,
Headley Road, Grayshott, Surrey GU26 6LG

Origination by: **Suburbia Design and Communications, Minafon, Green
Lane, Llangollen LL20 8TB**
Printed by: **Graphicom via dell'Industria – 36100 Vicenza, Italy**

Photography: **D J Murphy, Bob Atkins, Shutterstock.com,
Risto Aaltonen** (page 46) **Kit Houghton** (page 47).
Image of Charlotte Dujardin (page 11) courtesy of **Equipe**.
Front cover image by **Lucy King**
Illustrators: **Helena Öhmark and Rebecca Enström** (26, 52, 78),

PONY Magazine is published every four weeks.
To find out more about **PONY Magazine**, visit **www.ponymag.com**

PONY™

2014

The Annual

WHAT'S IN PONY The Annual 2014

p32

p92

p18

p44

p40

p8
p50
p36
p46
p80
p78

Let's gallop!

What's the big deal?
You might think that galloping is just a fast canter, right? Well – yes, and no! Galloping is a completely different pace. Canter is a pace of three-time, whereas gallop is a pace of four-time, where each hoof hits the ground separately, making its own beat. And it's fast!

Pick your moment
The best way to learn to gallop is with one other horse or pony, with a rider who is fully in control. An upward sloping field, with a big hedge at the top is the perfect place to gallop. The upward slope will slow your pony down and there will be no danger of you disappearing out of sight with that big hedge to stop you!

Gallop leg sequence
The sequence of footfalls with the left (near) foreleg leading is: *off hind, near hind, off fore, near fore.* With the right (off) foreleg leading it is: *near hind, off hind, near fore, off fore.* There is a moment of suspension when all four legs are off the ground.

Let's go!
Set off behind your friend (don't get too close), and ease into a canter. Now gently ask your friend to increase the pace, and nudge your pony along to keep up, leaning forward slightly, keeping your knees in and your heels down.

You're galloping!

Keep calm and be prepared for the speed – it's fast, and you may find your eyes are watering as you gallop along!

Are you ready?
If you're confident cantering in open spaces on your pony, or riding school ponies, and you can stay balanced, without holding onto your pony's mane, if you feel in control and can steer at canter, and jump, too, then you are probably ready for a gallop!

Get your position right
You can just lean forward when you gallop, but to get the most out of galloping and to help your pony it is best to adopt what's known as the *forward position.* This is what eventers do! Shorten your stirrups a couple of holes and, as your pony extends into gallop, shorten your reins, keeping your hands forward. Incline your shoulders forward slightly and lift your bottom out of the saddle, taking the weight on your knees and heels, keeping them supple.

Points to remember

Galloping is hard work for ponies, so make sure your pony is fit before you go charging about.

Ponies can get over-excited if galloping with friends. Try to avoid racing and keep your distance from others in your group to avoid accidents.

Pull up slowly after your gallop and give your pony a breather, turning his face into the wind. You could also loosen your girth a hole or two – but don't forget to tighten it before you head off again!

Check the going. Only gallop on suitable ground – neither too hard, nor too soft, neither rocky nor full of holes. Taking a fall at the gallop is not to be recommended. Resist the temptation to gallop in places unfamiliar to you – you won't know what's around the corner, or what the going is like.

Don't always gallop in the same place out riding – otherwise your pony will anticipate getting a wiggle on and *always* want to gallop there!

BOOST YOUR CONFIDENCE THE CELEB WAY

Nervous when riding? Worried about competing? Boost your confidence with these top riders' tips, and tips from Team PONY, too!

VISUALISE A TOP RIDER AND WATCH THEM RIDE A TEST THE NIGHT BEFORE YOURS.
Carl Hester MBE, dressage guru

NEVER OVER-FACE YOURSELF, ESPECIALLY WHEN TRAINING. IT IS MUCH BETTER TO KEEP AT A COMFORTABLE LEVEL AND ENJOY IT. ONLY PUSH YOURSELF WHEN YOU ARE FOCUSED AND YOUR ADRENALIN IS UP.
Piggy French, eventing idol

PREPARATION IS THE KEY. GET USED TO RIDING THROUGH AN ENTIRE TEST AT HOME ON A REGULAR BASIS, SO THAT RIDING A SEQUENCE OF MOVEMENTS DOES NOT COME AS A SHOCK TO YOU AND YOUR PONY.
Emile Faurie, dressage superstar

Try to stay relaxed. Imagine you are jumping at home or in your normal arena. They are the same jumps but in a different ring.
Daniel Nielson, fabulous show jumper

Repetition is the key to confidence, you must do it again and again and again until it is not a big thing and doesn't worry you anymore.
Oliver Townend, eventing guru

To give you confidence try taking your horse or pony for a lesson at a venue you have to travel to, or hire a school out and imagine you are at a show. Practise warming up and then run through your test at the end of your session.
Andrew Gould, International Dressage Rider

Give yourself plenty of time to warm up. If warming up for XC or SJ be careful not to over-jump your horse, a few fences is plenty and don't feel you have to jump anything big in the warm up - this is not the time to practise jumping big fences! Try to visualise yourself riding through the test or jumping the course in question beforehand. I find it really helps when you are in the ring to pretend you are at home in your own school or jumping field with nobody watching.
William Fox-Pitt, eventing extraordinaire

Just before you go down the centre line clear your mind of everything (boyfriends and homework!) and take a deep breath and focus on keeping your breathing steady and regular. Make sure you know your dressage test inside out so there is no fear of going wrong!
Charlotte Dujardin OBE, dressage diva

Remember that you are riding or competing for fun. As soon as you forget this there will be too many agonising moments!
Lucinda Green MBE,

Often the reason riders get nervous is the fear of the unknown and what might go wrong because they are focusing on the negative aspects. Devise a plan, arrive at shows early, visit shows beforehand and give yourself time to wander around. Have a set warm-up routine – these strategic points help to give you things to focus on and give you less time to think negatively.
Tim Stockdale, show jumping guru

Team PONY's top confidence tips!

If you get nervous, try singing a song to yourself. It means that you keep breathing and if you sing a silly song, then you'll relax, too!
Lucy

Visualise yourself being a top rider and competing at the standard you wish to be. The power of positive thinking can have a huge impact on your confidence!
Penny

Say to yourself to *Just do it!* What's the worst that could happen?
Janet

Think of a song and sing it in your head just before you enter the ring. But try not to forget the course because of it!
Tim Gredley, top show jumper

My top tip is mental rehearsal the night before. Go through step-by-step in your mind so you come up with a plan. Imagine yourself breathing deep and slow and your pony going fantastically. It's worked for me!
Kelly Marks, Intelligent Horsemanship behaviourist

A livery client leaves your yard.
MOVE BACK THREE SPACES

Take on a new yard assistant.
ROLL AGAIN!

Forget to turn the electric fencing back on.
MOVE BACK THREE SPACES

Be a Yard

Could you cope with being a yard owner? Your mission is to be the first person to reach the finish!

Win the Ya of the Yea awards!
ROLL AGAIN!

Order enough hay to see you through the winter.
MOVE FORWARD TWO SPACES

Fix some broken fencing.
MOVE FORWARD TWO SPACES

Your clothes get dirty tidying the muck heap.
HEAD BACK TWO SPACES

FiNiSH LiNE!

YARD ENTRANCE

You forgot to harrow the fields.
MOVE BACK TWO SPACES

12

How to play!

You need a die and each player needs a counter or coin. Each player rolls the die and the player with the highest number goes first. Start at the yard entrance and roll the die, moving your counter the correct number of spaces. Follow the instructions on the spaces as you go. The first player to reach the finish line wins! Have fun!

Blunt your clippers on a client's horse.
GO BACK TWO SPACES

Take a long lunch break.
MISS A TURN

OWNER!

Install electric fencing for laminitics.
MOVE FORWARD THREE SPACES

Leave the tap running and flood the yard.
MOVE BACK TWO SPACES

Organise a fun show at your yard.
MOVE FORWARD THREE SPACES

Buy a horse.
MOVE FORWARD TWO SPACES

Go on holiday and leave the ponies with someone else.
MISS A TURN

You can cut out and use these counters to play the game!

Breed File!
Cleveland Bays

Cleveland Bays have been bred since before the Middle Ages and are England's oldest horse breed! Read on to find out more!

Breed type

The Cleveland Bay is incredibly versatile and can turn its hoof to all disciplines. They are usually 16-16.2hh and are always bay, doh! They have a wide, deep body with strong, muscular loins. The quarters are also powerful and the shoulders sloping and well-built. The hooves are one of the most important features of the breed and should be strong and wide.

Cleveland Bays are always bay!

FAB FACT!
The Cleveland Bay Horse Society (CBHS) was started in 1884 to preserve and promote the breed, and that role is still carried out by the CBHS today.

Fab fact!
The Cleveland Bay originally came from the Cleveland area of North East England.

History

The Cleveland Bay is England's oldest breed of horse, excluding native ponies. Originating from the Chapman horse which was used by travelling salesmen, the Cleveland Bay was initially used to transport ironstone, potash and alum from the mines to the sea.

The Chapman horse and the Cleveland Bay were bred to be sure-footed and clean-limbed without feather. They were used extensively as a carriage horse. Her Majesty The Queen owns Cleveland Bays which are used to escort newly-appointed High Commissioners and Ambassadors. You can visit them at the Royal Mews in London.

A Cleveland Bay four-in-hand carriage!

Modern times

By the early 1960s there was only a handful of mature Cleveland Bay stallions in England and not many more mares with which to rebuild the breed.

Fortunately, Her Majesty The Queen gave the breed a big boost. Her grandfather had bred Cleveland Bays in the 1920s so, following in his footsteps, Her Majesty purchased a pure Cleveland Bay colt named Mulgrave Supreme.

Mulgrave Supreme was made available at public stud and the breed suddenly found a new lease of life as people flocked to breed their mares to him. Mulgrave Supreme produced many top quality horses competing in all disciplines, including some amazing Olympic level horses.

Nowadays, the breed is counted as Critical by the Rare Breeds Survival Trust. The CBHS has developed breeding programmes to ensure the long term survival of this historic horse.

A cute Cleveland Bay foal!

Cleveland Bays can compete in all disciplines

Famous ones

Spring Pascal is by the Hanoverian stallion, Pascal, out of a Cleveland Bay mare, Springtime Girl. Ridden by Samantha Thurman-Baker, they have their eyes fixed on riding at Grand Prix and even Olympic levels! Samantha is one of the top five junior riders in the country and is on the regional foundation squad.

Baydale Velvet was a CB X Arab. He was on the 2004 British Event Team.

Want to know more? Check out the Cleveland Bay Horse Society at www.clevelandbay.com

They are fast despite their size!

Cleveland Bays are royal carriage horses!

Part 1

Duggie's Dreams!

One day, at
PONY HQ...

Wow, that was a VIVID dream!

Hey Duggie – the farrier's here, time to come in and have new shoes.

How spooky is that? That's *exactly* what I dreamt!

Well spooky! Who would have imagined that was *exactly* what I just dreamt?

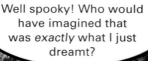

Get-outta-here!

Come back, Pierre!

Two dreams that came true – that can't just be coincidence. I must be psychic! Wow, I'm psychic!

Psychic! Whatever I dream comes true.

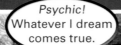

Yeah, sure you are and of course it does.

Hmmm, you must have fallen asleep in the sun, if you know what I mean!

Tee-hee!

Ha-ha!

The boys spend quite a lot of time just chilling in the field together. But sometimes...

Duggie

Soloman

The Colonel

Later

Hey Duggie, come and see this frog The Colonel has found!

Hmmph! Just dozed off there for a second and had another vivid dream. Must be something I ate...

I'm calling him *Pierre!*

Hey guys, I'm psychic!

Sick who?

Sigh-what?

I'll prove it. I'll tell you about the next dream I have, and I bet it comes true.

Yeah, why not. It'll pass the time.

I so miss Pierre...

The next day...

Wow, my most vivid dream yet! Can't wait for this one to come true! Hey guys, you'll never believe the dream I've had...

What has Duggie dreamt? Will Soloman and The Colonel believe him? Will Duggie's third dream come true? Turn to page 90 to find out in part two of *Duggie's Dreams!*

Could you cope in a crisis?

Would you be able to deal with a first aid crisis or know what to do in an emergency situation? Try our quiz to find how you would cope!

1

You've arrived at the yard to find your pony leaning all his weight back onto his hindlegs. What is your first thought?
a. He has colic
b. He has ringworm
c. He has laminitis.

2

What colour should your pony's mucous membranes be if he's healthy?
a. Pink
b. White
c. Yellow

3

Your friend's pony has come in from the field with a cut on his fetlock. What should you do?
a. Nothing – the air will heal it
b. Wash it, then bandage it tightly so it cuts off the blood supply
c. Hose it off, then apply antiseptic solution or call the vet.

4

Someone left the yard gate open and two ponies have escaped and are heading for the road! Do you...
a. ... panic and run in the opposite direction away from the ponies
b. ... shout for help, grab a headcollar and follow the ponies
c. ... race after the ponies on your own, thinking you can outrun them.

5

Your pony has a puncture wound on his hock joint. It seems small, but what should you do?
a. Call the vet – puncture wounds can be deceptively deep and your pony may need a tetanus jab
b. Stick your finger in it to see how deep it is, then you can decide whether to call the vet
c. Wash it and leave it open.

6

You've noticed worms in your pony's poo. Do you...
a. ... decide it doesn't matter because all ponies have some worms
b. ... keep an eye on it for a few weeks to see if it gets any worse
c. ... worm your pony with the correct wormer for the time of year.

Where should your pony's first aid kit be kept?
a. At home
b. At the yard
c. In the car.

7

Is your vet's phone number...
a. ... on your mobile phone and written on a board outside your pony's stable
b. ... in your head only
c. ... on the internet if you need it

8

Your pony is really lame and keeps holding one leg off the ground. Do you...
a. ... sob uncontrollably at how poorly he looks
b. ... walk your pony to the yard as fast as you can so you can call the vet
c. ... call your vet from the field, assuming it's safe for your pony to stay there.

9

Your horse trailer or horsebox breaks down on the motorway with your traffic-shy pony in the back. Should you...
a. ... unload your pony as quickly as possible and stand on the hard shoulder with him
b. ... go and wait in the back with your pony in case he gets stressed and throws himself around
c. ... check your pony is okay and then stay out of danger until the rescue service comes.

10

Your pony has managed to get himself cast in his stable and is totally stuck. What should you do?
a. Try lassoing your pony's legs from outside his stable so you can free him
b. Scream and panic your pony until he frees himself
c. Call for help and talk to your pony in a calm voice, but don't go into the stable because you might get hurt. Ask an experienced adult for further assistance.

11

How many breaths should your pony take per minute at rest?
a. 4-8 breaths
b. 8-15 breaths
c. 16-20 breaths.

12

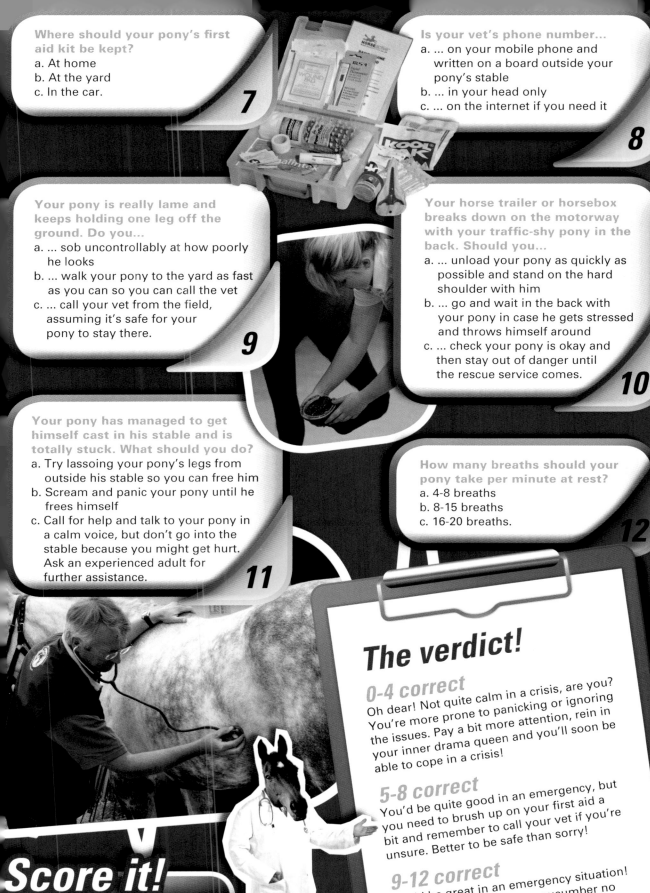

The verdict!

0-4 correct
Oh dear! Not quite calm in a crisis, are you? You're more prone to panicking or ignoring the issues. Pay a bit more attention, rein in your inner drama queen and you'll soon be able to cope in a crisis!

5-8 correct
You'd be quite good in an emergency, but you need to brush up on your first aid a bit and remember to call your vet if you're unsure. Better to be safe than sorry!

9-12 correct
You'd be great in an emergency situation! You're cool and calm as a cucumber no matter what's going on. Why not look into taking an equine first aid course so you can boost your knowledge even more?

More Than Just a Pony

by Heather Snowdon, aged 16

It was a cold, dull and cloudy morning. Emma opened her curtains to see that it was raining, too. Puddles were forming in the field next to her house. The weather outside very much reflected how Emma was feeling inside – down, upset and depressed. Emma was being bullied at school. No-one else knew about it. Well, no-one else except for Emma, the bully and her pony Harry. Emma told Harry everything. She often thought to herself that she wouldn't know what to do without her trusty loyal pony. She felt like Harry understood, that he got where Emma was coming from. Everyone said that horses couldn't talk and Emma knew that he couldn't verbally talk but she knew he spoke a different language, one of comfort, reassurance and guidance. Emma didn't know at this point but her pony's language was about to turn her life around for the better.

Emma got herself dressed and had her breakfast, but she wasn't very hungry. Her tummy had a knotting sensation inside as she knew what she was going to face when she got to school. The bully. Once Emma had managed to have a bit of breakfast she headed up to the stables to see Harry. He lived only a minute's walk away from Emma's house and was always waiting for her at the gate.

> Emma told Harry everything. She often thought to herself that she wouldn't know what to do without her trusty loyal pony

Today was no different. Harry greeted Emma with a lovely neigh as he stood with his head over the gate. Emma went and gave him a pat and then headed to the stable to get his feed. She made it up and took it out to him. Harry was eager for his breakfast and didn't take his head out of the bucket until he had finished it all! He was like a magnet to metal.

"I'll see you later Harry, hopefully today won't be as bad," Emma said drearily to her black pony, who was now munching on the haynet Emma had brought out to him. Emma gave him a quick cuddle. She loved giving Harry a cuddle. She loved that horsey smell that people who aren't into horses don't understand. As she snuggled into his chest Harry hung his head over her shoulder. He gave Emma a wee nudge on the back with his nose, as if he was cuddling her and setting her up for the day ahead.

"Right, I'd better go now Harry, bye," Emma said as she reluctantly left the field and headed back down to the house.

Once back at the house, Emma got her bag up together and headed out for the bus. It stopped just outside her house so she didn't have very far to walk. She stood with her hood up, waiting, with several others. Nobody really chatted in the mornings. It was all very quiet. The school bus came down the hill and pulled up at Emma's stop. She climbed up the steps with the others and found a seat. She took a deep breath and prepared herself for the day ahead.

After a 30-minute drive over the bumpy roads around Loch Moore the bus finally pulled up

Posed by model

outside the school gates. Everyone grabbed their bags and headed off the bus. Emma was one of the last ones to get off as she had noticed her shoelace had come undone and stopped to tie it. She headed through the gates and towards the door to the school.

"Oi, *you!*" someone shouted from around the corner. Emma recognised the voice.

"You wouldn't be ignoring me now, would you?" the voice continued, closer this time. Emma tried to ignore the voice as she knew it belonged to John. John was the boy who was bullying her. He was tall and had dark brown hair. He was in the same year as Emma but he was the tallest in the year and had a very intimidating voice.

"Just keep walking," Emma repeated to herself as she continued to walk towards the door with her head down. Suddenly, Emma got jolted backwards. John had grabbed the handle at the top of her rucksack and had given her a good tug. Emma gasped out of shock.

"Come here you!" John said angrily, dragging Emma round the side of the school.

"Now listen here, give me your homework to copy or you're not going to enjoy the next five minutes," John said in a horrible voice that scared Emma so much, she reached into her bag and desperately hunted around for her maths jotter.

"You're learning how this works, aren't you?" John continued, sneakily. He got out his jotter and began copying her answers. His jotter was scruffy, torn and looked like a dog had got hold of it, a vast contrast to Emma's clean and neat jotter. Once he had finished scruffily copying out Emma's answers he chucked her jotter back at her.

"Cheers!" he said as he winked one eye at Emma and walked off, all smug with himself. He walked away as if nothing had happened, leaving poor Emma desperately holding back the tears as she got herself together. She felt like she had a mountain forming in her throat where she was trying so hard not to cry. She took a deep breath and headed back towards the main entrance of the school and went in to begin her day of lessons.

Emma had no more encounters with John that day, except when she heard him call her a nasty name under his breath as they passed in the corridor. That tiny little word was enough to make the mountain start building in her throat again. It was horrible. Emma so desperately wanted to burst out into tears, she felt like she could cry enough to form a river! But she couldn't, she wouldn't, as this would mean that she'd have to explain what had been happening and that would mean John would give her a harder time. He'd already warned her of this. So she managed to clear her throat and continue down the corridor. Luckily, waiting for her at the bottom was one of her friends, who began to tell her about, what she thought, was a major and interesting story.

The final bell of the school day rang and all the pupils headed for their buses. Emma was so relieved when she sat down on her bus and the engine started. She couldn't wait to get home and give Harry a massive hug, she really needed it. Emma thought about what had happened that morning the whole way home, she couldn't get it out of her mind.

The bus arrived at Emma's stop just in time. Her eyes were full of tears and the mountain in her throat felt as big as Mount Everest. She got off the bus and ran to Harry. He was waiting for her at the gate. She ran into the field and threw her arms around his neck. She couldn't hold it in any longer and burst into tears.

"It was horrible, he grabbed me and pulled me back," Emma cried to Harry as her nose began to run. The tears were streaming down Emma's face. Harry stood and consoled Emma by cuddling her with his head. This was so comforting for Emma that she let out a big sigh and dropped her shoulders a little. They stood like this for a while and Emma gradually felt herself become a little more rational.

"Awww Harry, what am I going to do?" she said, letting her arms down from his neck now and standing looking at his head. Harry looked into Emma's eyes. Emma could feel him telling her that she really needed to tell her parents.

"I know Harry, I think I'm going to have to," she said. She gave her big, black cob another hug. As she snuggled into him she could feel that he agreed this was the best thing to do. Emma let out a deep breath and as if Harry understood Emma was releasing her stress, he snorted too! This made Emma let out a little giggle.

"Awww Haribo, what would I do without you?" Haribo was his nickname and Emma often called him this when they were having their more happier chats.

"Right!" Emma said to herself in an assertive manner. "Let's go."

She headed out of Harry's field and went to the stable to get his bucket of food and haynet. Once she had given him this and said her goodbyes she made her way back to the house.

"Oh hello love," her mum said, coming around the corner as Emma went through the front door. "Everything all right?" she asked as she usually did.

But this time, instead of saying everything was fine, Emma replied, "Actually Mum, there's something I need to talk to you about."

"Sure honey, no problem," her mum said holding her arm out for her daughter to follow her into the living room.

After about a 20-minute chat and lots of tears Emma had explained everything to her mum about John, and how he had been treating her. She felt so relieved to have finally told her mum everything. She felt like a massive weight had been lifted from her shoulders. They agreed to go to the school first thing in the morning and see Emma's guidance teacher together to sort the problem out right away. Her mum was really shocked about what had been happening and couldn't believe that her daughter had been managing to cope with this massive secret for so long without telling anyone. This was until Emma explained that she had been talking to Harry about everything that had been going on. Emma's mum wasn't really into horses and didn't visit Harry that often but she now had a whole new level of respect for him, realising how much he had helped her daughter through one of the most difficult times in her life so far.

He was definitely more than *just a pony.*

> Emma desperately held back the tears as she got herself together

> Harry stood and consoled Emma by cuddling her with his head

Time to rock!

Rocking horses are totally awesome, so we spoke to the Stevenson Brothers who have been manufacturing them since 1982 and are now the largest rocking horse manufacturer in the UK!

Rocking horse history

Rocking horses can be traced back to the Middle Ages! Back in those days, Hobby horses – a long stick with a fake horse's head attached – were very popular and children galloped around on them. In the 16th century, the hobby horse was superceded by the barrel horse which was a circular log on four legs with a fake horse head. Then, in the early 17th century, the first proper rocking horses appeared. Originally made from solid wood they were very heavy and easy to tip over, so they were then hollowed out. This not only made them lighter and more stable, it also allowed for a secret compartment to be built in the horse's belly! This compartment could then be used to store photographs, mint coins, locks of baby hair and other trinkets for future generations to find.

Rocking horses of all different shapes and sizes continue to be played with by children and adults all around the world.

An old fashioned hobby horse

This gorgeous rocking horse is made by the Stevenson Brothers

Behind-the-scenes

The Stevenson Brothers rocking horse workshop and hospital

Set up in 1982, the Stevenson Brothers sold 15 horses in their first year. All of the early rocking horses were dappled grey, a favourite of Queen Victoria, but the range was then expanded to include chestnut, bay and every other colour. Each rocking horse was given a brass plaque stating its individual number and the date it was made, which means that they can be identified easily.

In 1985, the Stevenson Brothers took their rocking horses on a world tour, attending trade fairs in London, New York, Boston, Dallas, Los Angeles, Sydney and Melbourne! Talk about travelling the globe!

In 1988, Stevenson Brothers rocking horses were first sold in Harrods and then they were commisioned to make a unique Merry-go-round for the Sultan of Brunei, who was the richest man in the world!

Your pony as a rocking horse!

The Stevenson Brothers offer a bespoke service, building a rocking horse to look identical to the owner's real horse. They can even use real tail hair from the actual horse and put their horseshoes onto the base! How cool is that?

The first Toytown rocking horse was made with Toytown's real mane, browband and horseshoes!

Pics: Stevenson Brothers and Shutterstock

This zebra rocker is super cool!

Famous rocking horses

There are a number of limited edition rocking horses including Zara Phillips' Toytown. The first one of these featured Toytown's own hair, browband and horseshoes! Wow!

Loads of celebrities own Stevenson rocking horses too, including Frankie Dettori! Even Mary King and Alan Titchmarsh have been photographed sitting on rocking horses!

Want to get close to the action?

Why not visit the Stevenson Brothers factory in Bethesden, Kent. The Stevenson Brothers also attend lots of events during the year, including The London International Horse Show at Olympia, so why not pop by their stand and see their amazing rocking horses for yourself?

Fab fact!

If you don't fancy owning a rocking horse, what about a rocking zebra like the one above, or even a tiger!

Make a mobile phone sock!

Not a sock that travels, but one which keeps your phone safe. After all, no-one wants to be without their mobile phone at the yard. Make a personalised sock for your phone!

HOW to do it!

1 Decide how you want to personalise your phone sock. The patterns on our sock suggested a stable door, so we put a pony in the stable!

2 Put your phone in the sock and cut across, between two and three centimetres above the phone.

3 Cut out the shape of the inside of the stable in black felt, then your pony's head, including his ears, in another colour. Glue these to the black square, and the black square to the sock.

4 Sew some wool to the pony's head for his forelock, and some more along his neck for his mane.

5 Stick on a tiny felt circle for his eye, and a semi-circle for his nostril. A tiny dot of white on the eye looks authentic!

6 Now just add a nameplate to complete your pony's stable.

FRAZZLE

7 Snip tiny slots in the top of the sock and thread a ribbon through so you can tie your mobile phone inside for safe-keeping. Your sock is ready to go!

FRAZZLE

Variations on a theme...

You can also make another holder from the same sock – taking the measurement from the top! Sew the bottom neatly together and glue on some felt horsey shapes and beads to liven it up – go mad! This phone sock has its own turn-up. Cute!

Sorted! One mobile phone holder!

I saved a pony's life!

Nancy refused to ignore a neglected pony in a field, despite her friend's scorn.

It must have been fate that made me take a different path home that day after school. It was a sunny evening and my friend Jade and I usually went the quickest way home, but this afternoon we decided to take the path around the park near the river. It wasn't a way I would go by myself – it was a bit lonely. I was daydreaming my usual daydream, pretending I had my own pony, when I saw something out of the corner of my eye, and turned to look.

It was a pony. A pony in the field overgrown with brambles. My heart leapt and I peered through the hedge to get a closer look, wondering whether there were others there, too.

It was alone. A chestnut pony with its head down, taking no interest in life at all. Its coat was dull and it didn't bother to flick away the flies which buzzed around its flanks. I could count its ribs and it looked thoroughly dejected – sad even. It didn't even point an ear in my direction when I made a clucking sound with my tongue. It was tethered, a rope around its neck, tied to a tree stump.

"Look, Jade!" I said. "A pony. I wonder how long it's been here?"

Jade followed my gaze but sighed. She wasn't into horses like I was. "Yeah," she said, "I see it. Do you think Jason Collins fancies me?"

I didn't care about Jason Collins. "It looks neglected," I murmured, looking around for signs of any care. The grass had all been grazed down and I couldn't see a water trough. "I think it's been abandoned," I continued, almost to myself, "and we ought to tell someone, to make sure it's all right."

"Oh it's only a horse," said Jade. "It'll be okay Nancy, you're such a worrier. Come on, let's see if that fabulous bag in the charity shop in the high street is still there."

There didn't seem to be much I could do about the pony but I lay awake for most of the night worrying about it. I wondered how long it had been there, alone and hungry. I wondered whether anyone else knew about it and whether its owner visited it. I couldn't forget the way it just stood there, its head low, resting a hind leg and looking like it had lost all hope.

STILL THERE

The next day I persuaded Jade to take the same route home after school.

"Oh, you're not going to go on about that horse again, are you?" she moaned.

"Come with me, Jade," I pleaded. "I don't want to go that way alone."

She came with me – and the chestnut pony was still in the field, its head down, like before.

> The pony didn't even point an ear in my direction when I made a clucking sound

"I'm going to report it!" I told Jade.

"Whoever to?"

"One of the horse charities. They'll check it out and make sure it's okay. If it is, then great. If not…" I left the sentence hanging.

"You're just meddling," Jade told me. "It's only an old horse."

A PHONE CALL

The woman at the charity took my details over the phone, asked where the pony was and promised that someone would take a look and that they'd get back to me to let me know. "Usually we find these cases are fine, but it's always a good idea to make sure, so many horses are being abandoned these days," she told me. "Thanks for your call."

I felt better knowing I had done something instead of just walking by, thinking it was nothing to do with me. When I went back past the field a few days later, the pony had gone.

> "You're just meddling," Jade told me. "It's only an old horse!"

WHAT A DIFFERENCE!

The charity phoned me back a few weeks later. The pony had been found dehydrated and starving. They hadn't been able to trace the owner, so had taken the pony into care and it was now getting healthier by the day. They had called her *Hope*, and they were confident she would recover fully and make someone a fabulous pony. When I told Jade she opened her eyes wide and gulped.

"You saved that pony's life!" she cried.

Six months later I persuaded my mum to take me to the charity to see Hope. I would never have recognised her – her coat was gleaming and she looked much bigger. But the biggest difference was in her eyes; she looked interested in her surroundings as she gazed around her and nuzzled my hand. She was full of life – nothing like the depressed and dying pony I had spotted in the field.

I'd been right not to believe that poor Hope was nothing to do with me. I'm so glad I had had the courage to call the charity and save a pony's life.

posed by models

27

Herd behaviour

You can learn a great deal about ponies by watching their natural behaviour, particularly how groups of domestic ponies interact in the field

Natural herd behaviour

Ponies are natural herd animals. In the wild, the main reason for any animal to live in a group is for safety. But even after years of domestication ponies still prefer to be in the company of other ponies.

It's long been thought that it was the stallion who led the herd but recent observation has proven that the leader is usually an older mare of the group. The stallion lives on the periphery of the herd and spends most of his time protecting the herd from predators and other stallions. The stallion keeps the herd together, and newcomers are not allowed into an established herd without the stallion's okay.

Don't leave me alone!

Ponies hate being alone and are able to form companionship attachments to other animals, including humans. Most ponies will become anxious and even depressed when left alone. They'd rather live with a goat than be on their tod!

Hierarchy

Within a herd there will always be a system of hierarchy which determines who eats and drinks first. With the lead mare and stallion dominating, all other members of the herd are part of a pecking order and must show submission to the ones that rank above them. As the herd dynamic changes – members die, foals are born and youngsters age – the pecking order constantly adjusts. Age typically determines rank, with the youngsters being at the bottom, but as they grow older, these young ponies will challenge the leaders.

Natural instincts

A pony's natural flight instinct is incredibly strong. Ponies will only really fight if backed into a corner, they'd always rather take the option to flee.

The instinct to graze is second only to the flight instinct. In the wild, ponies spend most of their time grazing, up to 20 hours of the day. This is known as *trickle feeding*. Ponies have very small stomachs in proportion to their body and can only handle small amounts of food at a time. This is why domestic ponies should be fed little and often, not one big meal, as their digestive system would not handle it well.

Using natural hierarchy in training

Natural pony behaviour can be used when backing and training ponies. To build a relationship with a human the pony must respect the human as a *herd member* who is higher in the social order. That will mean they will behave in a more appropriate manner towards all humans than a pony that has been allowed to engage in dominant behaviour over humans.

To have a successful relationship the pony needs to see its human as a leader. Wild ponies, and youngsters that have not been handled, view humans as predators, but they are naturally inquisitive and want to investigate things.

Ponies can be trained to do amazing things if they trust a person. Think about the Metropolitan Police Display team, those horses jump through fire!

Does your pony see you as a leader?

Even domestic ponies display certain herd behaviour, perhaps even with you! If your pony considers you to be higher up in hierarchy he might:

❀ Show signs of licking and chewing
❀ Have soft eyes and relaxed jaw
❀ Lower his head
❀ Not invade your space
❀ Yawn or blow through his nostrils, vibrating his lips

Sleepy time

Ponies can sleep standing up or lying down. They don't need solid, unbroken sleep like us. Short naps are fine! In the wild, ponies take it in turns to lie down individually or in small groups, so that others can keep a look out for predators.

Domestic herd behaviour

Domestic ponies that are turned out together as a herd will organise their pecking order by age and temperament, or both.
They are not so wary of lying down. A pony in a field on his own may well be able to lie down and snooze for ages. Well, it's not like he's going to get eaten by a lion or anything!

Communication

Ponies communicate with each other through mutual grooming, smell and vocalisation, such as whinnying, nickering and squealing. Body language is also important, such as ear position, head and neck height, stamping and tail swishing.

You can see ponies doing all of these things just by watching them socialise together in the field.

Having a pony to love means...

... you always have someone to share your troubles with.

... spending all your pocket money on your equine friend.

... getting up at the weekend before anyone else.

... you can follow your dreams.

... never being lonely.

... you know the difference between an Appaloosa and an Arab.

... knowing that your best friend is always waiting for you at the yard.

... starting the day with clean clothes and a dirty pony, and finishing the day with a clean pony and dirty clothes.

... persuading your parents to spend weekends driving you from show to show.

... sharing precious moments together.

... you feel like the luckiest person alive!

... cleaning tack when you could be out with your friends.

... a fluffy BFF!

10 things you need to know about Show jumping!

1 Walk it

Always walk your course. That way you can work out distances between fences and how many strides your pony will take, what the ground is like underfoot, and the best lines and approaches to fences. Try riding the course on foot – build a course with the jump wings but no poles and canter through the course on foot. You'll know it like the back of your hand!

3 Flags

Flags are used on show jumps so riders know from which direction the fence should be jumped. The red flag is always on the right, and the white flag on the left.

2 Get the correct lead

If you're jumping a course of fences you will be tackling jumps from both the left and right rein. Therefore you need to ensure your pony is on the correct canter lead at any given time. When you walk your course, work out which way you are turning to the next fence before you jump the previous one. That way you can open your rein over the fence to encourage your pony to land on the correct canter lead. If it doesn't work out, don't worry. Just come back to trot and pick up canter again when you're ready.

4 Canter on!

Getting a good canter is the key to getting a brilliant jump! Remember you want impulsion, not speed. Impulsion means controlled energy. To get this you want your pony to be between your hand and leg so that all his energy is contained. When your pony simply goes fast, all the energy and impulsion is lost out of the front end. You want to bottle up all that energy to use it over the fence.

5 Ground lines

This is a pole on the ground at the front of the fence. They are used to give the fence a base line to help ponies judge the size of the fence, and where to take off.

6 Five phases of jumping

There are five phases to jumping – approach, take off, moment of suspension, the landing and the get away. It is important that the rider stays focused and in balance at all five stages. It's particularly important that the rider maintains a consistent rein contact throughout so that they are neither jabbing the pony in the mouth, nor dropping the contact. A secure lower leg, strong core and good balance will enable the rider to stay in harmony with their pony through all five stages of jumping.

7 Up, up and away!

You won't do your pony any favours by looking down. You can't really tell what he's doing and it's likely that your position will be compromised. Always look up and ahead to the next fence. Look down at the ground and you might end up there!

8 Jump Cups

Never leave empty jump cups on wings – they are an unnecessary hazard. Don't leave them on the floor either, your pony could land on one and hurt himself.

9 Spreads v uprights

Spread fences are more appealing to ponies and can be approached at a more onward-bound canter. The back pole should always be higher than, or level with, the front pole so your pony can judge the height and width. If the back pole is low and wide, your pony won't see it until after he has taken off.

Uprights require a shorter and bouncier canter as you need your pony to jump high, not wide. The more poles, planks or fillers used will make the fence easier to jump. If there is only one single pole, a ground pole must be used so your pony can work out his take off point.

10 Know the rules

Knock down = 4 faults
First refusal = 4 faults
Second refusal = 8 faults
Third refusal = Elimination

Fall of rider = 8 faults
Second fall of rider = Elimination
Horse fall = Elimination

Good luck with your show jumping – the most important things to remember are breathe, smile and enjoy yourself!

PONY Puzzles!

Super Sudoku

Using the images shown, fill in the cells in the sudoku grid so that every column and row contains one of each image. Remember, none of the images can be repeated in the same row or column!

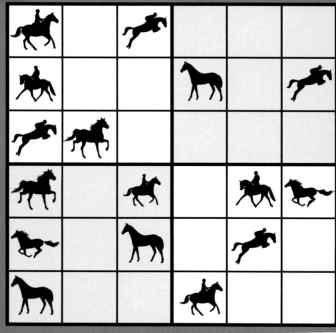

Unscramble the celebs

Can you manage to unscramble these riding celebs and guess the others from their photos?

1. FRAOTGNITTIHWSICNN
2. WILATIHWMAILKER
3. MAIKYRNG
4. CARSEHLTER
5. LAUTELLOCART
6. GEOEPSEIGRNCE
7. JONAPNAHTAGET
8. ZARLLIHPAIPS
9. ELLATIHWNEKER

Ridiculous Riddle

Can you work out the answers to these trick riddles? Make sure you think them through?

Riddle 1
A horse is tied to a 20 metre rope. There is a bale of hay 40 metres away from him. Yet the horse is able to eat from the bale of hay. How is this possible?

Riddle 2
An old King is dying and before he dies he wants to decide who will be the next King, his youngest son or his eldest son. He decides to hold a horse race for them both where the owner of the slowest horse will become the new King. He tells them that they must race to the castle and that whoever owns the slowest horse will become the new King. The youngest son jumps on a horse and starts racing for the castle. The King makes him the new King. Why?

Pic: Risto Aaltonen

10. 11. 12. 13. 14. 15.

Giant wordsearch

Can you find all these items of tack in our giant wordsearch? Look carefully – the words may be backwords or diagonal!

BIT
BREASTPLATE
BRIDLE
BROWBAND
CHIFNEY
CRUPPER
CURBCHAIN
FLASH
GIRTH
HACKAMORE

HALTER
HEADPIECE
LEATHERS
MARTINGALE
NOSEBAND
REINS
SADDLE
STIRRUPS
SURCINGLE
THROATLASH

g	y	d	n	o	s	e	b	a	n	d	t	t	o	k	s	u	d	n	a	b	w	o	r	b	r
l	a	r	p	i	b	p	o	n	e	a	h	n	m	a	r	p	r	b	a	o	n	e	d	h	b
i	z	t	w	l	n	u	l	e	e	n	i	m	m	a	r	t	i	n	g	a	l	e	n	r	c
t	e	n	h	a	o	k	h	d	i	r	i	o	j	e	b	b	a	a	t	h	n	i	i	i	r
r	q	m	f	r	e	t	l	a	h	l	m	a	r	w	a	b	r	i	d	l	e	t	l	m	u
e	b	h	p	s	o	h	m	f	n	a	s	a	i	b	s	p	s	h	e	m	i	l	c	s	p
i	i	e	a	c	y	a	u	n	i	y	c	s	s	i	h	s	t	a	e	r	t	e	y	t	p
n	u	a	i	k	e	r	t	a	s	n	e	k	s	s	k	h	p	i	h	d	n	x	s	r	e
s	s	d	c	a	l	o	r	l	c	c	e	c	a	r	t	p	a	m	h	r	n	s	c	e	r
t	c	p	s	h	s	n	l	n	a	y	i	h	t	m	r	u	o	n	a	l	y	z	y	b	z
h	a	i	e	e	d	r	f	m	o	s	n	o	p	o	o	l	o	n	r	f	m	c	e	o	i
j	i	e	c	n	i	m	a	l	o	s	h	n	c	i	n	r	l	e	r	e	n	t	a	e	l
s	o	c	o	m	a	n	e	b	l	c	u	r	b	c	h	a	e	n	p	m	i	a	c	r	e
r	h	e	o	m	o	s	o	u	i	r	l	u	o	n	s	e	h	p	j	s	a	l	r	s	h
a	a	i	p	r	s	t	i	r	r	u	p	s	m	a	e	v	i	s	k	a	h	g	a	u	t
f	j	d	w	l	e	l	a	p	g	m	i	m	y	j	v	w	a	s	l	a	c	e	n	r	r
j	e	n	f	a	d	e	h	i	i	e	g	o	s	e	i	l	f	s	s	a	b	g	r	c	i
e	q	m	f	j	e	a	u	s	d	h	s	a	l	f	i	a	r	t	i	u	r	t	l	i	g
k	b	h	p	g	o	t	a	g	l	c	n	a	i	b	c	p	r	o	f	c	u	l	c	n	a
e	i	w	a	n	n	h	u	k	e	a	h	s	s	n	w	a	i	r	r	r	c	e	y	g	b
t	i	f	h	i	a	e	a	r	r	b	e	i	s	a	g	y	f	r	b	e	e	x	s	l	a
l	s	i	c	p	l	r	r	a	s	r	e	s	f	d	i	c	a	a	s	a	d	d	l	e	r
a	c	u	l	m	n	s	l	n	z	i	b	h	x	n	u	w	h	c	a	l	n	p	y	b	b
h	a	t	e	u	d	r	f	m	c	d	o	t	f	s	e	e	h	d	r	l	m	c	u	o	e
l	i	r	r	j	i	n	e	t	r	l	v	a	s	a	t	y	n	i	m	o	l	i	g	r	i
b	r	e	a	s	t	p	l	a	t	e	r	b	w	s	c	g	n	a	i	c	u	l	a	d	n	c

Breed File!
Asiatic Wild Horse

Also known as the Mongolian Wild Horse or Przewalski's Horse, this is the only truly wild horse – the ancestor to our domestic horses.

Found you!

Although Nikolai Mikhailovitch Przewaski (a Colonel in the Imperial Russian army) is credited with discovering the Asiatic Wild Horse in modern times, and was honored by having the species named after him, these horses had evolved for millions of years before 1879 when he first came across them. Known as the *Takhi* by local Kirghiz hunters in the Gobi Desert, these ancient horses have roamed Asia for centuries. It is thought that the domestic horse evolved only some 160,000 years ago. It is the isolation of the Mongolian Wild Horse, in its harsh environment, which has kept it pure.

Hey good looking!

Asiatic Wild Horses all share the same physical characteristics and are all the same yellow dun colour. Only about 13hh, they usually have a dorsal stripe, and their black legs may also be striped. The mane grows upright, with no forelock, and both mane and tail have a harsh texture. The upper part of the dock is covered with short coat hairs before falling into a tail. The head is long and quite heavy for its size and the eyes are high and closer to the ears than domestic horses. The muzzle and coat around the eyes is paler than the rest of the body.

Spot the difference!

Don't try your luck!

The Asiatic Wild Horse is truly wild, and does not take kindly to domestication. Bad tempered, they have resisted all modern attempts to break and train them! Even so, they were probably the horses the Mongol hordes rode when they conquered the known world under Genghis Khan.

Fab Fact!

Przewalski's Horse has 66 chromosomes (which is their genetic material). Domestic horses have 64.

Fab Fact!

The horses drawn on the walls of caves by ancient man bear more than a striking resemblance to the Asiatic Wild Horse. They are the missing link between prehistoric horses and our own domestic ones.

Look familiar?

Famous on stamps!

Going home

Although the Asiatic Wild Horse is extinct in the wild, due to successful breeding programmes in zoos worldwide their numbers have increased in captivity. These zoos regularly swapped horses to reduce inbreeding. In 1992, 16 horses were re-introduced into their traditional habitat in Mongolia, and other herds have been released in the surrounding areas since.

Stripy legs and a dorsal stripe!

Great news!

You don't have to trek all the way to Mongolia to see these amazing horses because Marwell Zoo, near Winchester, has its own herd!

Phantom Racer

by Carrie Foley, aged 10

The bell sounded and the horses flew out of the stalls. Whips cracked and the crowds cheered excitedly. Number 22, a black stallion, was streaking miles in front, his heart pounding. Phantom Racer, his name was. And a phantom he was sure to be...

Jerry, Phantom Racer's rider, was grooming him late that night, a huge grin on his face when he thought of riding Phantom again. As he was thinking this his horse nudged him, suddenly unsettled. Jerry didn't see why and continued to groom him.

"I'll ride you, Phantom," he whispered, fetching Phantom Racer's tack and buckling it up. He began to lead him out when a large timber beam fell, blocking the exit. Jerry gasped. The beam was on fire – and so was the rest of the barn! As Phantom Racer whinnied Jerry leapt onto his back. The horse bucked and reared in fright, and Jerry went flying over the timber beam, away from danger. Phantom Racer, however, was stuck in the centre of advancing flames. The shrill whinny was the last sound of life heard in that barn for many years to come.

* * * * * * * * *

Jerry was safe, and although he had given up race riding completely, he still visited the track where he last raced. His wife, Harriet, was forever sitting silently in the living room, staring at the rosettes and photos of Phantom Racer, speechless in her mourning.

On one fine day Jerry decided to visit the track to watch a race. He placed a bet on the second-best horse, Starry Luck, the one who had always been a heartbeat behind Phantom Racer, and he wandered to find a seat. He sat at the front, where he knew he could watch easily, and mouthed the countdown he was so used to. Once again the bell sounded and the horses flew out of the stalls – only number 22 didn't open. Jerry had been told there had been a replacement horse due to race, but no horse emerged from the stall. All the other horses flocked together on the track and galloped for their lives.

Then Jerry saw something that changed his life forever. A misty white figure of a horse slithered out of the group of horses, and a faint white numnah with glittering clear numbers made Jerry feel light-headed. It was Phantom Racer... only he was... a *phantom!*

Jerry recovered quickly and watched in awe as the horse strained to beat all the others, passing Starry Luck effortlessly. Jerry cheered loudly and chanted the horse's name. Everyone around him thought he was crazy, but he continued to cheer anyway.

"Phantom! Phantom! Yeah!" Jerry roared, as Phantom Racer sped over the finish line. Starry Luck crossed it a whisker afterwards – and so Jerry won his bet. He was rewarded with thousands of pounds, and went home in a mood that could cheer up even his miserable old headmaster from his schooldays.

That night, Jerry woke to a familiar whinnying. He ran downstars and out the front door in his pyjamas and careered towards the stable yard, where he stoped dead. Phantom Racer was standing in the yard, his clear white eyes gazing calmly into Jerry's.

"Ph... Phantom?" Jerry stuttered, amazed.

Jerry, I am your Phantom Racer. A phantom I am indeed, but I am still your horse.

The horse strained to beat all the others

Jerry was almost certain he was seeing things. "No Jerry, you're not going nutty," he told himself, rubbing his forehead and closing his eyes tight.

Jerry, I am not a vision. I am really here. Touch me, I'll prove it!

"No... I can't..." said Jerry. "I won't believe it."

You won't touch your own horse? You lost me, now you've got me back yet you refuse to be grateful. Jerry, be strong and feel.

Jerry took a few deep breaths and reached out. Suddenly, his hand was rubbing gently against a soft muzzle

"Phantom, is it really you? It's really you!" Jerry cried, and went to hug Phantom. But he found himself on the ground, his arms wrapped around himself. When he looked up, Phantom Racer was nowhere to be seen. Jerry sat and stared in all directions. All he saw was blackness, no white figure. When he got up he heard a loud, clear ghost whinny coming from the sky. Jerry looked up at the stars and saw one was unusually large and bright. He smiled weakly and ran back to the house, stumbling as he went.

* * * * * * *

Months later Jerry found himself at the race track once again.

"I'll bet on Phantom Racer," Jerry told the shopkeeper, confidently.

"Sorry Jerry, you don't realise, do you?" the shopkeeper, Martin Andrew, grunted at Jerry, and chewed contentedly on gum.

"Realise what?" asked Jerry. "Oh yes, um... I'll place a bet on Nightstorm, then." Jerry mumbled and walked off.

"Jerry!" called Martin

Andrew, but it was too late, Jerry had already made his way to the racetrack. He sat down and watched as the horses shot out of the stalls. Of course, Phantom Racer's stall never opened, as every horse brought to it remained in shock, as if they'd seen a ghost... which they had. But as Jerry watched, Phantom Racer thundered out of the cluster of horses and made for the finish line. Jerry cheered loudly, chanting Phantom Racer's name, and yelled at the top of his voice. A man behind him tapped him gingerly. "Um, sir," he said, "The horse Phantom Racer is dead."

Jerry, I am your Phantom Racer. A phantom I am indeed, but I am still your horse

"Nonsense! Phantom's immortal!" Jerry screamed, still punching the air.

When the race was over, Jerry slipped quietly into Phantom's stall. "Hey Phantom," he whispered. He heard a gentle whinny reply, followed by a faint white figure forming in the far corner.

Jerry, you came. What are you doing here? You know members of the public are not allowed here. But seeing as this stall is now abandoned except for me, you are in no danger. I won, did I not? Phantom spoke in Jerry's mind.

"I guess you're right, but can you visit me tonight? Jerry asked, stroking Phantom's nose.

Never ask anything from a ghost... Phantom whispered, and Jerry found himself stroking thin air. He wiped his eyes, crying with delight to have seen his friend up close again, and made his way home. That night, Jerry was

restless, listening intently. All he could hear were the barn owls in the wood, nothing else.

Jerry, a voice said.

"Phantom?" Jerry called.

You wished to see me tonight. You asked, so you may not see me, but we may talk. I am all around you. That may sound unsettling but fear not my good friend. I think you are frightened, Phantom declared, and a warm breeze passed Jerry.

Phantom was breathing on him, Jerry decided, as another puff followed the first.

Very impressive. Shall we head out to talk in the freshness of the countryside air?

"Of course," Jerry replied, He pulled on his coat and boots and wandered downstairs and out the back door.

"Why can't I see you?" he asked.

You know the answer to that question. You asked me to visit, which is against the laws of ghost and human contact.

"I'm sorry, I won't again, but please try to visit as often as possible," Jerry pleaded, hanging his head.

I will forgive you on this one ocasion, but never again will I let you off.

Jerry knew he had done wrong, and was deeply sorry. He paced the bedroom once he got home, whispering and muttering to himself so much, his wife had to repeat herself several times before he heard her.

"Jerry, what's

wrong?" she asked.

"Phantom Racer," Jerry replied, not paying much attention.

"Goodness Jerry, you need to relax about the horse. Yes, he was your main interest but you know he's gone. Forever."

Jerry ignored her, showing no sign of belief. Of course he was right not to believe her. Jerry didn't see Phantom again for ages after that day, but every night he lulled himself to sleep by believing he would see Phantom that night.

* * * * * * *

It was just two weeks after Jerry stopped wishing that he met Phantom again.

"Phantom! What took you so long?" he asked.

Phantom stared at him coolly, and then then replied.

Don't you see? Foolishness has overtaken you, Jerry.

"But I missed you. I wanted to see you so much."

Jerry, it is all part of the punishment.

"You said you'd forgive me."

I did, but even so it requires a small punishment. Now the punishment is complete you are allowed to see me. Shall we ride?

Jerry clamberd onto Phantom's back. They went off together into the midnight-black sky, happy to be together.

Maybe, if you're lucky, Phantom Racer might just appear to you...

When he got up he heard a loud, clear ghost whinny coming from the sky

Posed by models

Make a fab pony keyring!

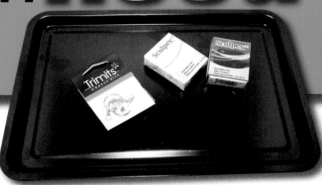

This cute keyring is simple to make, but great fun!
Why not make some for your bessie mates!

You will need

Oven-bakeable clay
Keychain
Oven tray

HOW to do it!

1 In your chosen pony colour, roll one big ball of clay for the body, a medium-sized one for the head and four small round bits for the feet.

2 Stick the clay pieces together to make your pony shape. Next create a mane and tail, plus ears and any markings out of clay and stick them on.

40

3 Attach your keychain to the top of the body by folding it under the clay. Make sure it's firmly in place!

4 Bake the clay in the oven according to the instructions on the back of the packet. Ask an adult to help with this and be very careful – the keychain will be red hot! Allow it to cool and there you have it, a funky new keyring!

Many thanks go to Equine Market Watch for this idea.

We will NOT look away

emw

www.emwuk.org.uk

Charity 1114700

EMW-UK is a charity with a dedicated equine sanctuary in Herefordshire. To support their amazing work and to buy their amazing pony keyrings, go to **www.emwuk.org.uk**

41

IS YOUR STABLE UP TO SCRATCH?

WHY DO I NEED TO CLEAN?

Having a clean, tidy yard will help keep your pony healthy. Bacteria are tiny, single-celled organisms which in large quantities can sometimes be harmful to your pony. Bacteria love to multiply in urine, droppings or rotting food so if you keep your yard clean, they aren't something you'll need to worry about.

FEED TIME

You wouldn't eat your dinner off a dirty plate, so why should your pony? Scrub out his feed bowls after each use to prevent leftover food going mouldy. Not only will this keep your pony healthy, but it will also make his food taste better!

SOME BACTERIA ARE GOOD AND AID DIGESTION IN THE GUT.

BRUSH AWAY BACTERIA

Every pony should have his or her own grooming kit as sharing brushes can lead to cross-contamination of bacteria. Therefore if one pony has ringworm, for example, it can be easily spread on brushes.
What can you do?
* Make sure your pony has his own grooming kit. Write your pony's name on your brushes so you don't get them muddled up.
* **Wash your brushes at least once a month using warm water and washing-up liquid.**
* You can now buy special brushes that kill bacteria.
* **Make sure that your pony also has his own saddlecloth and headcollar. The saddlecloth should be washed regularly to kill any bacteria.**

WONDERFUL WATER

Your pony's water should be changed daily so that it is fresh. Remove the water bucket while you muck out so that dust doesn't build-up and scrub the bucket once a day. Don't forget to clean out the water trough in the paddock, too!

POOR QUALITY HAY AND BEDDING OFTEN CONTAINS HIGH LEVELS OF DUST AND FUNGAL SPORES THAT CAN CAUSE YOUR PONY BREATHING ISSUES. BUY DUST-FREE BEDDING TO ENSURE HIS LUNGS ARE KEPT HEALTHY!

MUCKING OUT MATTERS

Mucking out should be done every day. You wouldn't want to sleep on a dirty bed, so why should your pony?

What can you do?

✳ **Remove all droppings and wet bedding daily and replace with fresh bedding.**

✳ Once a month, throw all the bedding to the sides of the stable and disinfect the floors – make sure to use a brand that is safe for your pony. While you're waiting for it to dry, remove any cobwebs or dust.

✳ **If your pony is kept on rubber matting, remove any soiled bedding that has become trapped. Wash and disinfect the mats once a month, too.**

TACK ROOM TACTICS

It's not just your pony's stable that needs to be kept clean, but the rest of the yard, too.

What can you do?

✳ **Keep the yard, feed room and tack room tidy. Sweep the floors and remove any dust or cobwebs.**

✳ Keep feed in containers that are waterproof and vermin-proof.

DYK?
AMMONIA IS A COMPOUND OF NITROGEN AND HYDROGEN FOUND IN URINE. IT CAN CAUSE BACTERIAL INFECTIONS IN THE HOOVES, SKIN SORES AND ILLNESS.

GRAB YOUR COAT!

Your pony's rugs can also collect bacteria, so they should only be used by one pony.

What can you do?

✳ Wash your pony's rugs regularly or send them for specialist cleaning.

✳ **Use a summer sheet under your pony's rugs – this is easier to clean regularly and won't need re-proofing.**

PEST CONTROL

Yard pests can include rats and mice, both of which carry diseases. Rats and mice aren't fussy where they urinate, so they will often urinate on hay, bedding or on feed if they can get access to it. Totally gross!

What can you do?

✳ Ask your yard owner to use bait boxes or traps to catch vermin. Or get a yard cat!

DYK?
THERE ARE SPECIAL WASHING MACHINES DESIGNED FOR HORSEY ITEMS THAT USE COLD WATER TO PREVENT SHRINKING, BUT STILL KILL BACTERIA.

Remember, keep it clean and stay healthy!

What horse breed are you?

Follow our fab flowchart to find out what breed of horse you are most similar to!
Start here!

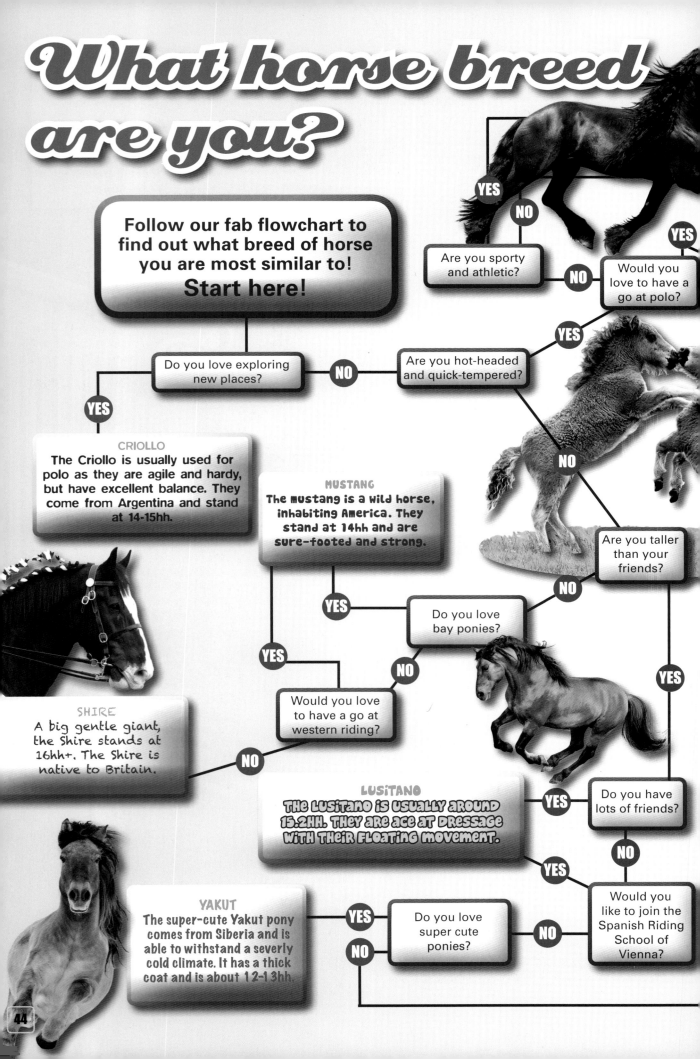

Do you love exploring new places?

NO → Are you hot-headed and quick-tempered?

YES

Are you sporty and athletic?

YES

NO → Would you love to have a go at polo?

YES

NO

CRIOLLO
The Criollo is usually used for polo as they are agile and hardy, but have excellent balance. They come from Argentina and stand at 14-15hh.

MUSTANG
The mustang is a wild horse, inhabiting America. They stand at 14hh and are sure-footed and strong.

Are you taller than your friends?

NO

YES

Do you love bay ponies?

YES

NO

Would you love to have a go at western riding?

YES

NO

SHIRE
A big gentle giant, the Shire stands at 16hh+. The Shire is native to Britain.

LUSITANO
The Lusitano is usually around 15.2hh. They are ace at dressage with their floating movement.

YES → Do you have lots of friends?

NO

YES

Would you like to join the Spanish Riding School of Vienna?

YAKUT
The super-cute Yakut pony comes from Siberia and is able to withstand a severly cold climate. It has a thick coat and is about 12-13hh.

YES ← Do you love super cute ponies?

NO ←

NO

CONNEMARA
The Connemara comes from Ireland and stands around 14.2hh. They are hardy but make excellent show jumping ponies. Duggie and Soloman are both Connemaras!

ARAB
The Arab is usually around 14.3hh with a dainty build. They are perfect for endurance riding but can be highly-strung!

FRIESIAN
THE FRIESIAN STANDS AT 15HH+. WITH A LONG, FLOWING MANE AND TAIL AND HIGH-LEG ACTION, IT'S A POPULAR DRESSAGE HORSE!

Do you run away if you're scared of something?

NO — **Do you enjoy dancing?**

YES — **Would you rather be with friends than on your own?**

YES

Would you ditch your friend for someone who is more popular?

NO

YES

YES

EXMOOR
The Exmoor pony stands at approximately 12hh. Hardy and bred on the moors, they make great all-round ponies.

NO

SHETLAND
THE SHETLAND IS NO BIGGER THAN 42 INCHES AND MAKES A CHEEKY, BUT FUN, FIRST PONY!

Do you enjoy the thrill of cross country riding?

NO

WELSH COB
THE WELSH COB, ALSO KNOWN AS A WELSH SECTION C OR D, STANDS 13.2HH+. THEY HAVE A HIGH KNEE ACTION.

NO

Do you love the thought of having a go at scurry driving?

YES

YES

Do you prefer to live in the countryside?

NO

CASPIAN
One of the oldest horse breeds in the world, the Caspian is normally 10-12hh. They are perfect for riding and driving.

NO

GYPSY COB
Also known as a Tinker cob, the Gypsy Cob is of Irish descent. They have long, flowing manes and tails and are usually piebald or skewbald.

YES

APPALOOSA
THIS SPOTTED BREED STANDS AT 14.2-15.2HH. THEIR MANE IS OFTEN SPARSE. THEY ARE COMPACT AND STRONG.

OUR 2012 DRESSAGE DARLING CHARLOTTE DUJARDIN!

2012 really did belong to one girl... the amazing dressage talent that is Charlotte Dujardin! Find out how she went from amateur rider to Olympic gold medallist in just five years.

HOW IT ALL BEGAN...

Born in London and brought up in Hertfordshire, Charlotte first rode a pony when she was just two years old and was bitten by the riding bug instantly. Charlotte was always competitive, especially against her older sister, and she worked her way up through the Pony Club. She went from lead rein and first ridden to winning showing classes at Horse of the Year Show and Hickstead by the time she was 16.

Charlotte was always a fantastic all-round rider, but it soon became clear that she would excel at dressage. Leaving school at 16, she went to work for top dressage rider Judy Harvey for four years and bought her first proper dressage horse with some inheritance from her grandmother. Her voyage into the world of professional dressage had begun!

MATCH MADE IN HEAVEN

In 2007, Valegro (Blueberry as he's know at home) was one of several young, novice horses on Carl's yard. Charlotte was given the job of bringing on the five-year-old gelding for Carl to compete should he show enough promise.

The pair shot to unexpected success when they won their grand prix debut in January 2011. A quick succession of wins led to them being selected to represent Team GB at the Europeans in Rotterdam in August alongside her mentor, Carl, riding Uthopia. Suddenly, things were moving quickly for Charlotte and Blueberry, and before they knew it they'd won team gold at the Championships!

The dream team ended 2011 winning the FEI World Cup Grand Prix at London Olympia with 81.043 per cent – a personal best for her and Blueberry.

MEETING MR HESTER

Charlotte had always admired top British dressage rider Carl Hester and in February 2007 she got the opportunity to have some lessons with him.

Charlotte spent 10 days training with Carl and it's safe to say that he spotted some serious talent in the young Charlotte! He offered her a job as a groom at his yard and she's been there ever since – except that nowadays, it's Charlotte giving the lessons and training to other riders, including eventing legend Mark Todd!

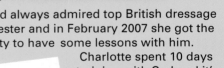
Lovely Carl

OLYMPIC DREAMS

The icing on the cake came for Charlotte and Valegro when they were selected to represent GB at the London 2012 Olympic Games. True to form the pair stormed the competition and in the first round the partnership set a new Olympic Record of 83.784 per cent!

On 7th August GB won the gold medal in the team dressage event and two days later, Charlotte and Blueberry won the gold medal in the individual dressage event with a score of 90.089 percent!

"Blueberry is a horse of a lifetime. Carl gave me the ride on him when Blueberry was just five years old. When it became clear that he had immense talent I expected Carl to take the ride for himself. But as he saw my partnership grow, Carl let me keep the ride and words cannot describe how grateful I am for this opportunity."

A WELL DESERVED ACCOLADE

In March this year, Charlotte received the OBE from Her Majesty The Queen. What a hugely exciting and special way to top off the most amazing five years – going from amateur rider to Olympic Gold medallist.

Well done Charlotte – Team PONY thinks you rock!

How to...

We know what to do and when to do it. Do you?

... use a mirror in the school

Mirrors are great for checking your position in the saddle, and for seeing whether the pony you are riding is straight (or not, if you are doing lateral work). This means that even when you are schooling alone, you can get more out of it as you can be your own instructor!

... tighten your girth

- Keep your feet in your stirrups.
- Put your reins and stick in one hand – don't let the reins go into loops, and don't drop them!
- Lift your knee and put your leg forward to free up the saddle flap.
- Lift the saddle flap with your free hand. Lift the buckle guard, too.
- Now you can pull up the girth with your free hand, guiding the tongue of the buckles into the new hole. When you are used to it, you won't even have to look!
- Run your hand under the girth to make sure everything is flat.
- Now replace the buckle guard and flap, put your leg in the right position and take back your reins. Sorted!

... make much of your pony

Instructors may ask you to *Make much of your pony*, as you ride on a lesson. This means giving your pony a pat and thanking him.

Simply pat or stroke your pony on his neck or shoulder, telling him he's done a good job! That's all there is to it, and it acts as an incentive for your pony to try his hardest for you. Everyone wants to be thanked for their efforts!

... pass someone in the school

This isn't as tricky as some people make out. The rule is simple: always pass another rider left-hand to left-hand, that way everyone knows what they should be doing.

Don't forget that if you are schooling in a school with others, any slow work should be done away from the outside track, leaving it free for anyone who wants to school in a faster pace. That makes sense, doesn't it?

... let your pony have a wee!

Ponies often decide to have a wee when they get to the school. Why? Because the surface is soft and absorbant, and their legs won't get splashed!

Ponies need to stand still for a wee – and will adopt a stance to let you know. If your pony starts stretching out his front and hind legs, he's telling you he's busting! Don't ride him forward – it's not healthy for him to keep going. Instead, quietly stand up in your stirrups, holding onto his mane if it helps you to balance. This takes the weight off your pony's back, allowing him to have a wee in comfort!

(Ponies don't need to stop for a poo – they can canter and even jump passing dung at the same time, so you don't have to worry about that!)

... ride leading file

Don't panic, *leading file* is the name given to anyone riding at the front of a ride. If you are asked to ride leading file remember these important points:

● You are responsible for the pace – and everyone behind you will be struggling to keep up if you go too fast. Keep a brisk, but not fast, pace.
● Use the corners of the school. If you cut the corners, the ride will get left behind.
● Take a look behind you now and again, to make sure everyone is happy with your pace.
● Keep a constant pace – no speeding up or slowing down.

So now you know how to do these, too!

Jobs for the horses!

There are horses and ponies all over the world working for a living – including riding school ponies! Here's a small selection!

Horses work the land

Many farms all over the world still depend on horses to plough the land and pull farm machinery. These three horses are working in Belgium – so are probably not the only horsepower on the farm! Some enthusiasts love to keep alive old traditions, and horses can be seen at competitive old-style ploughing matches, providing a taste of times gone by. Look out for ploughing matches near you – but make sure they are not using tractors!

Horsepower!

In the USA, the Amish is a religious group of people which does not use any modern machinery – which includes cars! Original horsepower comes into its own, and the roads are full of these wagons which families travel around in!

Cow sense!

The best way to tend herds of cattle on the huge ranches of America is still by using cow ponies. These hard-workers, usually Quarter horses, possess an inate cow-sense, which means they easily pick up their tasks and have almost an in-bred instinct for how cattle think and behave. Some brilliant cutting horses can even work without a rider, cutting out a steer from the rest of the herd, in the same way a sheepdog will work sheep!

Fancy a horsey holiday with a difference?

There aren't many travelling gypsies using traditional caravans these days, but you can still hire one for a holiday with a difference! Training in horse care and harnessing up is provided on the first day, and then it's just you, the horse and the open road for a holiday you'll never forget!

Horses and the City

If you've ever been across the pond to New York you may have seen the carriages pulled by horses in Central Park. Popular with tourists, the work of these horses is carefully regulated, and operators are licenced. It's a great way to see the city and the park!

Ride him cowboy!

Bucking broncos are the big draw at rodeos. It may seem like a hard life but in reality the horses work for only a few seconds at a time, and many are famous for their ability to send an experienced cowboy flying. The rodeo riders draw lots to see who will ride which horse – and they obviously hope they will get one which can't buck so hard and viciously as the famous ones!

'Ello, 'ello, 'ello...

Police forces all over the world appreciate the value of horses on their staff. Providing a presence which is intimidating to those on foot, these well-trained, equine police personnel are indispensable at football matches and anywhere where a quiet show of strength is needed for crowd control. They also provide a brilliant PR opportunity – everyone loves to see a police horse!

ingle bells

nowy regions a horse-drawn sleigh is en the best way to get around – not to ntion the most exciting! The horses need cial studs in their shoes to prevent them m slipping on the snow and ice and if u are going for a sleigh ride you need to p up warmly! But what a great way to oy the snow.

War horses of today

Thankfully, horses are no longer used in warfare, but there are still regiments all over the world which retain their mounted units for ceremonial occasions. Our own Household Cavalry's duties includes guarding Her Majesty The Queen, and tourists still flock to see the mounted guards at Horse Guards Parade in London.

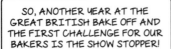

SO, ANOTHER YEAR AT THE GREAT BRITISH BAKE OFF AND THE FIRST CHALLENGE FOR OUR BAKERS IS THE SHOW STOPPER!

FOR YOUR SHOW STOPPER WE WANT YOU TO BAKE... A GINGERBREAD HOUSE.

YES! I'VE PRACTISED THIS.

WOW CHARLIE, YOU LOOK LIKE YOU KNOW WHAT YOU'RE DOING.

THIS IS GOING TO BE THE WINNER!

SO CHARLIE, WHAT ARE YOU MAKING TODAY?

MY GINGERBREAD HOUSE IS THREE STORIES HIGH AND HAS A PITCHED ROOF AND EVERYTHING!

IT'S A LOT OF WORK, WILL YOU FINISH IT?

I HOPE SO!

OKAY BAKERS, TIME IS UP!

PLEASE BRING YOUR CAKES FOR JUDGING.

LET'S START HERE...

MMMM, VERY GINGERY.

IT'S DECORATED WELL, TOO.

GOOD FLAVOUR...

BUT IT LOOKS A MESS!

WOW CHARLIE, THIS IS IMPRESSIVE!

THANKS PAUL. IT'S MY OWN RECIPE. I HOPE YOU LIKE IT.

THIS TASTES DISGUSTING!

THERE'S NO SUGAR IN IT!

I DEFINITELY PUT LOADS OF SUGAR IN!

I THINK YOU MIGHT HAVE MIXED UP THE SUGAR AND SALT, CHARLIE!

OOOOPS!!!

They thought anyone could ride my pony

Harriet didn't realise how much her riding had improved – until somebody else rode her pony

Everyone thinks my pony, Widget, is an easy ride. The thing is, he is always well behaved – now. I got Widget when he was only four, and he was determined to challenge everything I asked him to do. When I tried to ride him out on a hack he would nap. When I rode him in the school he would pretend to be terrified of the doors, the walls and the surface. When I took him to his first show, he just stood by the collecting ring and refused to move, let alone go near a jump!

But I persevered with Widget because I knew he had potential (and I loved him!). And gradually, I learned to ride him and he learned to trust me, and now we have a great bond and he'll do practically anything for me. But it took a long time – and when I changed stables, no-one at Forest Farm Livery had seen Widget at his worst. They only saw him now, at his best.

> I persevered with Widget because I knew he had potential (and I loved him!)

I hadn't been there long before the comments started:

"It's easy for you, Harriet, because Widget's so good at jumping."

"You don't know what it's like to have to ride a naughty pony."

"I wish I had a pony like Widget, who just does everything like clockwork!"

I couldn't believe it – they should have seen Widget on his worst behaviour! I suppose it was a compliment in a way because now Widget was brilliant and I could take some credit for that. But still the other girls seemed jealous of my pony. Or of me.

THE PONY CLUB RALLY

Things came to a head at the Pony Club Rally. I was in a group with three other girls from Forest Farm, and it was our turn for some dressage practice. It didn't help that our instructor, Maggie, held up Widget and me as a good example. The looks on the other girls' faces were getting more and more fierce.

Finally, Jessica could stand it no longer. "It's all right for Harriet," she whined. "*Anyone* could do a good dressage test on *Widget*."

"I think it would be a good idea if we all tried riding each other's ponies this morning," Maggie said. I didn't know how I felt about someone else riding Widget, but I decided it would be good for me to have a go on another pony. It had been a while. The other girls' faces lit up, and they *all* wanted to ride Widget.

"Hmmmm," mused Maggie, "I think Jessica can try riding Widget."

So we swapped. A smug-looking Jessica mounted my surprised pony and I rode Jessica's black gelding, Licorice, who was always reluctant to go on the bit and refused to bend. I was concentrating so hard on Licorice that I couldn't take much notice of Jessica riding Widget. Maggie asked me to ride a short test on Licorice and although he threw his head up a couple of times he did at least try to bend for me, and he dropped onto the bit for most of the test. I patted him and rode him over to the others, who were open-mouthed.

"Well done, Harriet," said Maggie, grinning at me. "Now it's Jessica's turn."

REALISATION DAWNS

I watched as Widget reverted back to his old, unco-operative self. He snatched the reins out of Jessica's hand, dropped onto his forehand and performed his test with his quarters swinging in and out all around the arena. Jessica couldn't ride him for a toffee. I was amazed and realised not only was Widget brilliant now, but I was actually a better rider than I had thought.

> "It's all right for Harriet," Jessica whined. "Anyone could do a good dressage test on Widget."

We swapped back, and Jessica looked sheepish. She finally understood that the rider had more to do with Widget's performance than she had thought.

"Sometimes," Maggie said quietly, "a rider is doing much more work than we give them credit for."

I heard no more nasty comments from any of the girls after that – either at the rally or at the yard. They realised that Widget wasn't such an easy ride after all!

I rode Jessica's black gelding, Licorice

posed by models

WELL DONE TODAY GIRLS. YOU ALL WORKED REALLY HARD. NOW LET'S PUT THESE PONIES BACK IN THEIR STABLES.

MEL'S SUCH A GOOD INSTRUCTOR ISN'T SHE?

YEAH, SHE'S GREAT.

I'VE LEARNED LOADS FROM HER.

MEL, YOU AREN'T LEAVING ARE YOU?

I'M AFRAID SO. BUT DON'T WORRY, I'M SURE YOUR NEW INSTRUCTOR WILL BE FINE.

NEXT WEEK

HI, MY NAME'S KATE AND I'M YOUR NE INSTRUCTOR. I'VE BEEN TOLD ABOU EACH OF YOUR RIDING LEVELS, SO LET'S GET STARTED!

THAT WAS A BIT MEAN!

WAS MY POSITION REALLY THAT BAD?

NO! I DON'T KNOW WHY SHE SAID THAT.

WHY IS SHE BEING SO MEAN TO ME?

GRACE, YOU'RE SLUMPING IN THE SADDLE AND YOUR REINS ARE TOO LONG! COME ON, SORT YOURSELF OUT!

GRACE, SKY AND CARLA HAVE BEEN HAVING WEEKLY LESSONS TOGETHER FOR AGES. THEIR INSTRUCTOR MEL IS FAB BUT SHE HAS SOME BAD NEWS FOR THE GIRLS...

CARLA   GRACE   SKY

THANKS FOR EVERYTHING. I'LL REALLY MISS SOME OF THE RIDERS HERE.

WHAT DO YOU THINK MEL MEANT BY THAT?

YOU DON'T THINK SHE'S LEAVING DO YOU?

SHE SEEMS OKAY...

OK, LET'S SEE YOU ALL GO LARGE AROUND THE SCHOOL.

SKY, CARLA, THAT WAS GOOD, BUT GRACE, YOU WERE ALL OVER THE PLACE! YOUR POSITION WAS AWFUL!

SKY, CARLA, THAT WAS OK. GRACE, YOU'VE GOT A LOT TO WORK ON OR YOU'LL HAVE TO DROP DOWN A CLASS.

WHY IS SHE PICKING ON ME? I THOUGHT I WAS AS GOOD AS YOU TWO. I'M NOT COMING BACK NEXT WEEK, SHE'S HORRIBLE!

YOU MUST COME BACK! YOU HAVE TO STAND UP TO HER!

KA-POW!

FACE YOUR FEARS

NEXT WEEK

CUTE!

CARLA   GRACE   SKY

OH NO! HERE SHE COMES!

I HOPE YOU'RE GOING TO PUT IN A BIT MORE EFFORT TODAY GRACE.

NOW THE PONIES ARE WARMED UP, LET'S SEE YOU CANTER TO THE REAR OF THE RIDE. GRACE, YOU CAN GO FIRST.

GRACE, THAT'S JUST AWFUL!

I'VE HAD ENOUGH OF THIS!

GRACE LOOKS READY TO EXPLODE!

OH DEAR!

YES, I'D LIKE THAT.

WELL DONE GRACE! THAT WAS SO BRAVE!

THANKS, I'M SO GLAD I STOOD UP FOR MYSELF!

THE END!!!

STARRING: JESS AS GRACE, SOPHIE AS SKY, EMILY AS CARLA, JANE AS MEL AND JULIEANNE AS KATE. PLUS BEANIE, CERYS AND HARRY THE PONIES! ! LOCATION: MANOR FARM, HANTS

57

THE QUESTIONS

How will horses feature
in your future? You
don't have to be a top
rider to ensure that you
have a horsey life. Try
our quiz to find out in
which direction your
talents and interests
could take you

1. Which of these images mostly reminds you of you?

2

Which of these activities would you most likely be doing when you are not riding or at the stables?

- Playing with my model horses
- Drawing and painting horses
- Shopping with my mates
- Cleaning tack

3

What do you see when you look at this image

- A river, two trees and some birds
- Two circus horses
- A horse's skull
- Fighting rabbits

4

If you could have any holiday which would you choose?

- A course on creative writing and drawing – with the focus firmly on horses, of course!
- A riding holiday in the Scottish Highlands?
- A city break where you can buy stuff?
- A holiday on an American ranch, rounding up horses?

5 Your number one horsey day out would be...

- ... visiting a horse charity and meeting the residents
- ... a day at PONY Magazine, learning how the magazine is put together
- ... visiting the Utterly Horses Hullabaloo!
- ... a day shopping – with no limits!

6 Which of these ponies appeals to you the most?

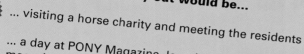

7 Which of these horsey personalities do you admire the most?

8 If money (and talent!) were no object, at which of these horse sports would you most like to excel?

THE VERDICT

Mostly red You're so horsey, you might just like a more traditional horsey job with the horses themselves. Groom, instructor, farrier, vet, stud groom, veterinary nurse, equine physio – the list goes on and on!

Mostly yellow You're a bit of a girly girl, but there are still some careers within the equine industry you might like. For example: Equestrian fashion (design or retail), Public Relations working for equine clients and thinking of ways to promote their products. Or how about working for Horse & Country TV?

Mostly purple You're creative and arty and you could combine your love of all things creative with a career involving horses. Good career choices could include: Equestrian journalism, equestrian artist or photographer.

Mostly green You're a bit of a dreamer, aren't you? How about working in the equestrian travel industry? There are plenty of holiday places here, and even more abroad. It would be like being on holiday all the time – only harder work, and they pay you, instead of you paying them!

59

Lisa and the Mysterious Note

When Lucy and her pony Ginger went for a ride, it was the start of a great adventure!

by Lucy Megan Tiplady, aged 11

One bright, sunny day, Lisa tacked up her best horse from the riding stables to go on a hack. She was extremely excited and simply couldn't wait!

Lisa always took care of Ginger at the riding stables, no matter what happened. She had blonde hair, which was as curly as the waves, millions of freckles spread around her face and was always brave and confident, which gave Ginger a big confidence boost. Ginger was a skewbald who loved to go flat-out and, most of all, loved to jump! Lisa thought she was born to ride the gorgeous horse. Ginger was raring to leave the stables straight away. Lisa knew which way he wanted to go (which was the canter track). They had been on it lots of times before and she could tell it was Ginger's favourite ride! When Lisa had finished tacking up, she hopped on and they both walked on together.

You would have thought that Ginger was a racehorse! He was flying up the road like a bolt of lightning, but Lisa didn't mind one bit, as she loved to imagine how it would feel to ride a real racehorse!

In no time at all they were at the start of the canter track, but then, out of the blue, Ginger did a humungous shy, which came so suddenly, Lisa fell off. The poor shocked girl got up and wondered what Ginger had shied at. She was

brave and wasn't hurt, but she wanted to know what had caused Ginger to react in such a way. Lisa saw something moving in the hedge. She walked over, leading Ginger, and found a crumpled note flapping in the breeze. Excited, she opened the note and read it eagerly. This is what it said:

> To Jimmy Westwood
> I've found the gold you wanted me to find. It's hidden at Hill Top Wood, underneath the berry bush. The box has got everything in it you wanted, but you still haven't paid me, so hurry up with the cash!
> Harry Williams

Lisa was speechless. Could she beat this Jimmy Westwood to the gold, or was it just a fake note? Lisa had no idea! Instead of going for a blast along the canter track, she could gallop through the fields to Hill Top Wood. If no evidence of gold was there it wouldn't matter because she would still have enjoyed a good old gallop!

Could Lisa beat this Jimmy Westwood to the gold, or was it just a fake note?

Lisa trotted Ginger steadily while scanning the note just one more time. It was quite ripped and wet, so it must have been there for quite a while. Lisa knew she must hurry as Jimmy Westwood could nearly be there, so instead of trotting she thought she had better speed up to a fast canter to beat the horrible-sounding man.

As quick as a blink, Ginger was

at Hill Top Wood. Lisa never knew Ginger could go that fast! She was really proud of her one-in-a-million skewbald. She started to search for any berry bushes she could see, while her ears were listening out for any sound of Jimmy Westwood. Ten minutes later Lisa had searched every bush – and then she saw a dark figure looming through the trees.

Quickly she led Ginger into the forest, hoping the person wouldn't see her and, luckily, he didn't. Lisa moved around Ginger to see if she could see any more and, to her amazement, something shiny caught the corner of her eye. She went cautiously over and was completely astonished to see a metal box, not padlocked or bolted, but simply closed with a little piece of string. Lisa went nearer and was surprised to see how small it was. It had gold spilling out of the edges and it shone radiantly in the sun.

As it was small she thought she would be able to carry the box between Ginger's mane and the front of her saddle. Lisa quickly lifted the treasure box and placed it carefully on the front of her saddle and Ginger didn't mind a bit. Lisa mounted with a bit of a struggle but as they walked on Jimmy Westwood apppeared suddenly through the trees and caught sight of the treasure box he had been looking for. The angry man was as fuming as a hungry lion that had lost its prey. As for Lisa, she was too shocked for words.

"What do you think you are doing, little girl, with that there box?" screamed Jimmy Westwood with rage.

"W...well, I...I Just s...saw this b...b...box," Lisa replied.

"It's not your property, you know you're stealing!" roared

Jimmy Westwood.

"I w...wasn't s...s...stealing it," exclaimed Lisa.

"I have a good mind to lock you up!" shouted the cross man, the wrinkles on his forehead as white as snow. Stepping towards Lisa he tore the treasure box from Ginger's saddle and dragged poor Lisa off her startled pony.

Lisa tried to struggle away but it was no use. Jimmy yanked her and Ginger to a grassy area. Then he pulled up a piece of long grass and an underground opening appeared. It was pitch black, with rats and bats scurrying about. Lisa screamed in horror at the thought of taking one step into there, but as the horrible man was so strong he easily forced Lisa in and left Ginger tied to a tree.

Jimmy Westwood had thrown Lisa into a cave like a piece of dirt, and she began crying her eyes out. "What can I do now?" sobbed Lisa. "I'm never going to see my best pony again and I can't see a thing. Oh, this is so unfair!"

The only sound Lisa could hear was water dripping, and once or twice she felt a rat running past her. Cautiously she got up and walked a little, hoping she wouldn't step on a rat! She held her hands in front of her and continued to walk until she found another passage with a flicker of light shining dimly in the distance. Putting her aching arms to her sides, Lisa walked towards the light.

"Please be a way out," she repeated quietly to herself. "There must be a way out if I can see light."

Soon, Lisa reached the source of the light but unfortunatley, she couldn't fit through the gap. When she looked out of the hole she saw she was on the outskirts of a busy village. She believed it was Hill Top Wood Village. Lisa was astonished that she had managed to walk as far as she had. She thought the village was at least two miles away from where she had started out, but that didn't matter now.

"Help! Can anyone get me out of here?" shouted Lisa with all her might. Suddenly she saw a tall man with wavy blonde hair and eyes as blue as the sea.

"Please help me to get out of here," said Lisa, beginnning to calm down a little.

"Oh course I will," said the man, pushing something aside that blocked the entrance, and helping the dazzled Lisa out.

"Thank you so much!" said Lisa, jumping around and enjoying the sun and fresh air.

"My pleasure," said the man, and Lisa could see he was wearing a police uniform! She immediately told him all about finding the note, Jimmy Westwood capturing her, and finding her way along the passage to call for help.

"Would you like to help me find this evil man?" asked the police officer, walking to his car.

"Well, I'll come for a bit," replied Lisa, "because Jimmy Westwood left Ginger, my amazing pony, tied to a tree and as he is really well behaved he is probably still there." Lisa hopped into the police car with its flashing sirens.

The policeman and Lisa sped towards Hill Top Wood. Soon, they were nearly at the top of the hill but then, suddenly, they stopped as something was blocking the road.

"Ginger!" shouted Lisa, as she flew out of the car. "I was worried I'd never see you again!" She gave him a hug and a mint from her pocket. As Lisa mounted Ginger he set off like a bolt of lightning with the police officer following them.

"What are you doing, Ginger?" asked Lisa, who was worried she would fall off. "Whoa, steady there!" she said, trying to calm him down. But Ginger wouldn't go any slower, he just went faster and appeared to take no notice of Lisa at all.

Suddenly, Ginger stopped and Lisa slid off. As she did so, a shadowy figure caught her eye. With the policeman behind her Lisa said, "Excuse me!"

The man turned around and Lisa and the policemen could see that he was putting gold into black bags. It was Jimmy Westwood!

The policeman wrestled a pair of handcuffs on Jimmy Westwood.

"Or should I say George Wigford," said the officer. Pushing him into the car the officer turned to Lisa.

"Thank you very much," he said. "If it wasn't for you and Ginger I wouldn't have caught this dangerous thief. We've been looking for him for years but I suppose his hiding place has been underground, where he put you."

Lisa felt extremely pleased, and proudly said, "We wouldn't have found Jim..., I mean George Wigford, if it wasn't for my beautiful Ginger. He deserves all the praise, don't you Ginger!" Ginger lifted his lip and looked as though he was trying to smile. Then he munched on the grass as he stood next to his best friend Lisa.

"I can't wait to tell my friends about this," said Lisa. She picked up Ginger's reins, waved goodbye to the policeman and rode off back to the stables.

> "What can I do now?" sobbed Lisa. "I'm never going to see my best pony again and I can't see a thing. Oh this is so unfair!"

> As Lisa mounted Ginger he set off like a bolt of lightning

Posed by model

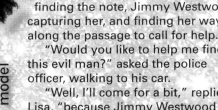

Breed File!
Extra cute Exmoors!

Cuddly bear of the equine world the Exmoor pony is one of the nine British Native breeds and a super little riding pony!

The ancient breed

Exmoor ponies are one of the oldest equine breeds in the world and are the closest thing we have to the original wild horse – the Asiatic Wild Horse, who we talked about on page 36!

The Exmoor is an entirely unique breed of pony which has lived on Exmoor for way longer than people have. The first written record of Exmoor ponies is in the Doomsday book, which was compiled in 1086. The breed has remained pure since prehistoric times, mostly due to the remoteness of its environment which meant there was no influence from other horse breeds.

In 1921 the Exmoor Pony Society was formed in an effort to keep the breed pure following fears that it could get "lost in the genetic melting-pot of breed improvement".

A novel idea

In the 1930s the Exmoor became incredibly popular as a children's riding pony, partly due to the success of the book *Moorland Mousie,* which told the tale of an Exmoor pony.

DYK?

According to The Rare Breeds Survival trust the Exmoor pony is *at risk*. It is currently classified as endangered, meaning there are only 300-500 registered breeding mares in the UK.

Fab fact!

The Exmoor pony has a distinctive jaw formation and the beginnings of a seventh molar – something no other equine breed has!

Exmoor ponies on Porlock Hill, Somerset

Breed type and temperament

The Exmoor pony is a great example of a true type, which has evolved in response to its environment.

They are always bay, brown or dun with black points. They have no white markings but instead have cute mealy markings around the eyes and muzzle. They usually have lighter coloured tummies, too. They stand between 11.2-13.2hh.

Exmoors have some excellent design features to protect them against harsh weather:

* **An ice tail (or snow chute), which is a thick fan-like growth of short hair at the top designed to keep his bottom warm and dry!**
* **A ridge of flesh around the eyes known as toad eye.**
* **A double-layer winter coat. The underlayer is soft and downy and the outer layer is thick and waterproof.**

They truly are a product of their environment!

Can you see the brand mark on this mare's shoulder?

FAB FACT!
Pure bred registered Exmoors are branded with a four-point star on the near shoulder.

Are they wild?

There are no truly wild ponies in the UK today. All ponies that roam on Exmoor are owned by someone. However, Exmoors are often used for conservation grazing. They are very hardy and able to thrive in all sorts of habitats from high moorland to bogs. They are selective grazers with great teeth, and while they like the sweet young grass, they will also tackle gorse, purple moor grass, soft rush brambles and thistles. Exmoors are being used for conservation grazing by The National Trust, Natural England and County Wildlife Trusts.

PONY Puzzles!

Odd one out

Can you circle the odd one out in each of these groups?

1. Carl Hester, Charlotte Dujardin, Laura Bechtolsheimer, Tim Stockdale
2. Bib, Trace, Blanket, Stocking
3. Pastern, Fetlock, Coronet, Croup
4. Body, Dandy, Flick, Tail
5. Dressage, Show Jumping, Cross Country, Bareback
6. Bay, Chestnut, Spotted, Milk
7. Frosted, Snowflake, Fewspot, Dalmatian
8. BEF, BHS, FEI, BSP
9. Connemara, Hackney, Dartmoor, Andalusian
10. Duggie, Soloman, Colonel, Major

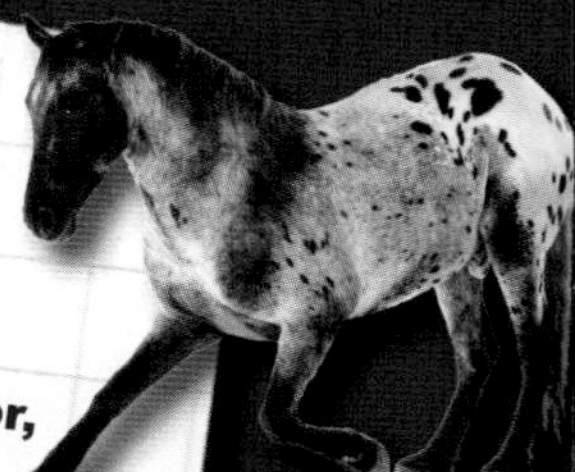

Perfect Pairs

Can you manage to pair-up these words?

1. RACING
2. MANGALARGA
3. IRON
4. STRAWBERRY
5. CLEVELAND
6. SHOW
7. FREESTYLE

A. GREY
B. BAY
C. JUMPING
D. MARCHADOR
E. DRESSAGE
F. ROAN
G. SILKS

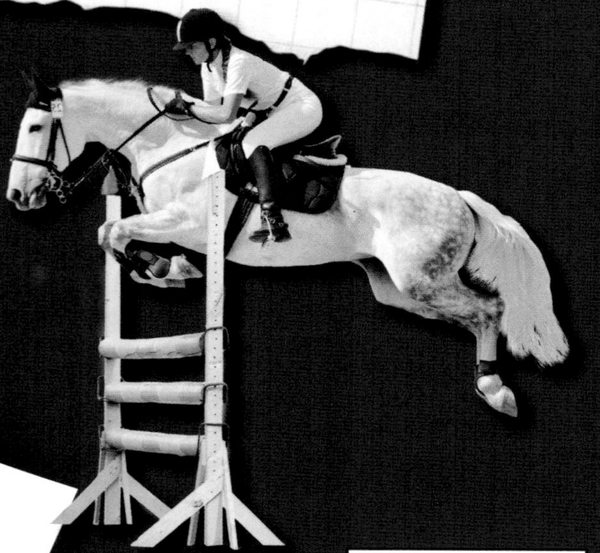

Point taken!

Can you work out which pony point goes where?

SHOULDER
CROUP
POLL
CREST
FETLOCK
CORONET
MUZZLE
RIBS
THROAT
EYE
PASTERN

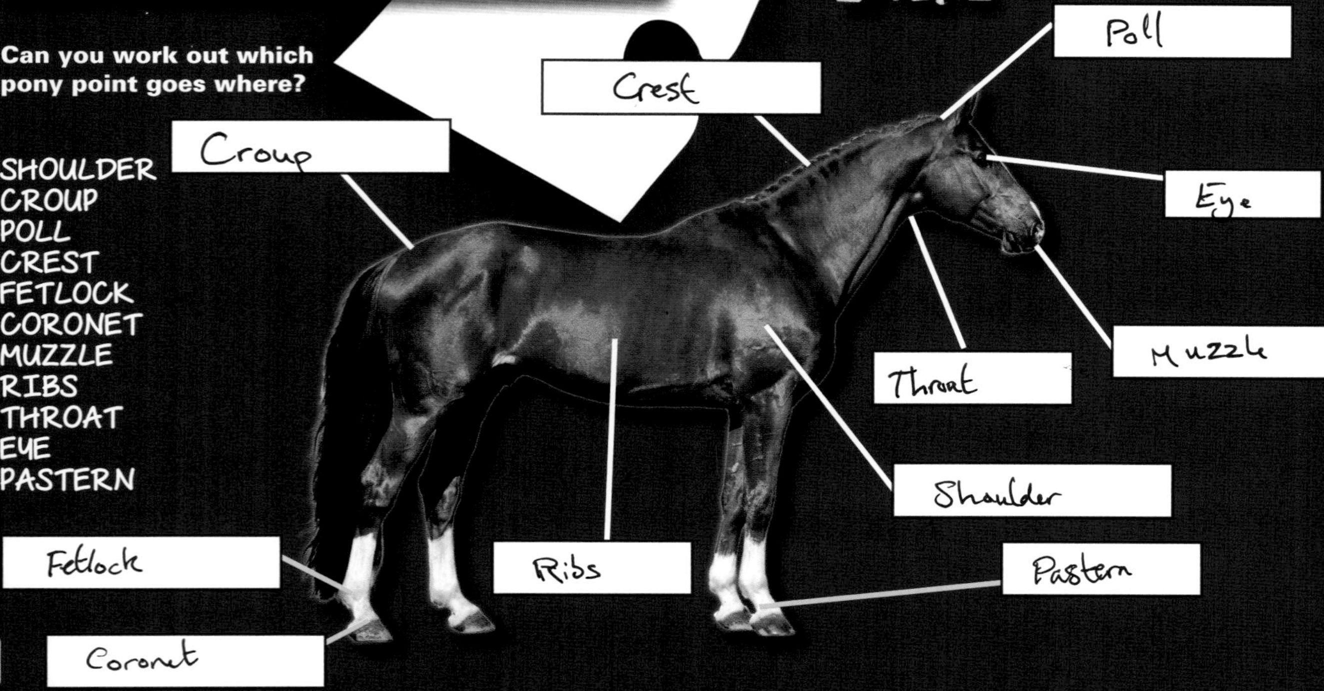

Poll

Crest

Croup

Eye

Muzzle

Throat

Shoulder

Ribs

Pastern

Fetlock

Coronet

Great gridwork

Can you fit all of the following rare breeds into the grid?
Be careful – some of them may fool you!

CASPIAN
CLYDESDALE
DALES
DARTMOOR
ERISKAY
EXMOOR
FELL

HACKNEY
HIGHLAND
KABARDIN
KONIK
MAREMMANO
MARWARI
SHIRE

Answers to all the puzzles can be found on p98!

PONY Poetry!

Here are some more of ou[r]
Highly Commended poems
from the PONY Poetry
Competition featured in the
Spring 2013 issue of PONY.
Maybe you'll be inspired to
write some poetry

TEN FRIENDLY HORSES

by Emily Dinning (10 years)

Ten friendly horses,
Grazing in a line,
"Hacking!" said the rider,
Then there were nine.

Nine friendly horses,
One knowing it'll be late,
"Competitions!" cried the eventer,
Then there were eight.

Eight friendly horses,
Staring up to heaven,
"Shoes!" boomed the farrier,
Then there were seven.

Seven friendly horses,
Learning different tricks,
"Racing!" shouted the jockey,
Then there were six.

Six friendly horses,
Feeling so alive,
"Grooming!" yelled the owner,
Then there were five.

Five friendly horses,
Eating more and more,
"Check up!" groaned the vet,
Then there were four.

Four friendly horses,
Waiting for their tea,
"Clipping!" moaned Mum,
Then there were three.

Three friendly horses,
Waiting for you,
"Hunting!" said the huntmaster,
Then there were two.

Two friendly horses,
Mother and son,
"Feedtime!" called the boy,
Then there was one.

One friendly horse,
Looking so fine,
Her name is Dizzy,
And she's all mine!

LONE HORSE

by Eloise Abraham (14 years)

His eyes were sad, his mane was tangled
His coat was coarse and muddy and mangled
His hooves were badly overgrown and cracked
He had no muscle; he was not schooled or hacked
You could see his bones, his ribs stuck out
His field was bare as if there'd been a drought
He wanted love and warmth and trust
Instead he was surrounded by mud and rust

But after years of suffering and pain
He's no longer stuck in a field in the rain
He has a warm stable, he has a rug
He has a friend to give him love and hugs
He's no longer thin and hungry and weak,
For he found the love that he once did seek

THE CLEVER FOAL

by Aileas Colthart (12 years)

The clever foal,
Just look at him go,
Born not an
hour ago.

The clever foal,
Just watch him play,
As he watches for
the day.

The clever foal,
Just watch him learn,
His master's love he
will earn.

The clever foal,
Watch him sleep,
A watchful eye his
mum does keep.

The clever foal,
Just look at him go,
All bright and
ready for the show.

MY PONY

by Frances Allan (14 years)

I love my pony and my pony loves me,
But not in the way of sitting in a tree,
I hug him and kiss him and muck out his stall
And hang up his haynet on the stable wall,
But this is not love and like it may be,
For he, his name is Peewee, cannot marry m[e]

STRIDING TIME

by Imogen Murfin (13 years)

The wind on the moors blows low,
As the golden glint in the pony's eye becomes stronger.
The hoof marks he leaves,
Are like the trail of a treasure map.
The treasure he seeks,
Makes the pounding of his heart stronger.
And the little tick-tock in his mind,
Reminds him of how little time he has left.
His muscles grow weaker and the wind blows stronger,
But still he carries on.
Every stride he makes,
Reminds him of the path that awaits.
The ghostly moors fight back,
But the pony is not done yet,
And still the tick-tock grows louder and stronger,
As the pony becomes weaker and weaker,
But still he carries on.

CROYDE

by Annabel Hunt (14 years)

This is the ride that swept me away,
Over the hills and around Croyde Bay.
Riding over the sand dunes, luckily no rain,
Astride a pony, Tally was her name.
Cantering along tracks, what a breathtaking view,
I said to my escort, "I can't believe it's just me and you!"
Back off the beach and along the path,
We did some long trots and had a good laugh.
Why does the ride have to end, it feels like
it's only just begun,
But maybe that's down to Tally, as we've
been having so much fun!

Happy

1 Why do we hack out?

There are lots of reasons really. Mostly because it's fun to be out in the open, exploring with your equine BFF! The fresh air is good for you both and it's a great way to relax and unwind.

Schooling can get pretty boring – for you and your pony! Varying his work with hacking will keep him happy and interested in being ridden.

Hacking is a great way to get a pony fit. You can build up the speed and distance that you ride slowly over time to increase a pony's fitness and stamina. And because you mostly ride in straight lines when hacking out, it's not as strenuous for the pony as lots of turns, circles and schooling movements can be.

2 Teaching good manners

Now here's the mega important bit – teaching your pony to be the perfect hack! Hacking out is all about having fun and relaxing, so you want your pony to be super-polite. A pony that jogs, bolts, naps or won't stand still is, quite frankly my dear, no fun at all! Here are some things your pony should do, and tips on how to teach him to do them!

🏵 **Stand still while you mount, and when you ask him to. It's actually not difficult to teach ponies to stand still, it's just a matter of repetition. Ask a friend to hold your pony while you mount, and do not allow him to walk off while you swing your leg over the saddle. He must stand stock still until you ask him to go. Be consistent in your training and your pony will soon get the idea!**

🏵 Open and close gates. Now this does take some practice, but if your pony is responsive and moves away from your leg aids without question, you should be able to get the hang of it in no time.

🏵 **Go first or last. Not all ponies like to lead but they really must be able to. It's all about trust. If your pony trusts you, that's half the battle won! And someone always has to go at the back – so why not you? Take it in turns with your mates so that no-one is always at the back.**

🏵 Not pull, jog or lag behind. These are all linked to your pony being polite and respectful, which are things you can begin to teach in the school.

hacking

Hacking out on your fave pony is just about the most fun thing you could do! Here are our top five ways to make sure you have the best hacking experience EVER!

3 Where to go and what to do

It's a wonderful idea to hop on your fave pony and ride wherever you want but there are some rules to adhere to. Stick to bridle paths and common land where horses are allowed. Don't ride on footpaths or on private land, and always remember to close gates behind you.

Try to vary your rides so that it's more fun for you and your pony. Why not spend some time with your friends researching the internet and looking at maps for rides you could try.

Do you have a trailer or horsebox? Why not box-up your pony and head off for pastures new? If you don't own a trailer you could always borrow or hire one.

4 Bond with your pony

Use your time hacking as time to bond with your fave pony. For a start – give him a break! Don't expect him to work in an outline, let him stretch his neck and relax because hacking should be a fun experience for you both.

Talk to him, or even sing to him! Most ponies love the soothing sound of the human voice. It makes them feel calm, relaxed and reassured by us. A scratch and a pat on his neck or wither won't go amiss either!

5 After your ride, offer your pony a treat to say thank you for such a nice time.

FESS UPS!

FARTY FACE!

I was grooming my pony's tail one day ready to go to a show. As I chatted to my best mate Tilly about the cute guy at school, my pony let off a massive fart in my face! It smelt revolting and I stank of it all day! Gross!
Rosellen

MEGA EMBARRASSMENT!

FLYING FAECES!

I was riding my pony Pipsqueak bareback to improve my balance. I asked him to canter, but as I gripped on for dear life he kept going faster and faster. Suddenly I flew out of the side door, straight towards the muck heap and ended up aquaplaning through the poo at the edge of the heap! It was totally rank!
Ellie

EPIC EMBARRASSMENT!

POOPY PROBLEMS

My friends and I were helping out at the yard in the hope of spending some time with the totally hot yard crush, Jake. My friend Tina suddenly patted me on the back, but I wasn't sure why until the end of the day. As I took off my jacket, I realised Tina had wiped poo off her hand onto the back of my jacket and I'd been walking around in front of Jake with a big poo stain on my back! I was *soooooo* annoyed with her!
Lana

EPIC EMBARRASSMENT!

POOEY PONY CLUB

At my first ever Pony Club Camp we were all camping in the fields next to the ponies and I was dared to throw water over our instructor's tent. As I crept towards the tent and threw the water, she popped her head out and the water splashed all over her face, leaving her spluttering and furious! I got a huge telling off and had to poo pick all the fields at the yard instead of riding – it took ages!
Simone

MEGA EMBARRASSMENT!

HERE ARE OUR TOP FESS UPS OF 2013!

BIRDIE BONUS

My pony Blue and I were out hacking in our local woodland last year when we decided to take a shortcut. As Blue pushed through the trees we must have disturbed a bird's nest. The angry bird flew around us squawking in horror and then did a gross pooey dollop on the top of my hat! It took me hours of scrubbing to get the mark off. I won't be taking that shortcut again in a hurry!
Cat

EMBARRASSING!

WEEING-WOE

My pony Savannah and I were at our first show and I was really excited. I'd spent hours grooming her and cleaning my tack in preparation but as we lined up in the middle of the ring, she started to fidget. Thinking nothing of it, I ignored her. The judge came up to speak to me and Savannah started to wee, splashing it all over the judge's clean boots! I was so embarrassed, but I couldn't even leave the ring because Savannah was still weeing! She took ages and by the time she stopped I thought I'd die of embarrassment.
Deanna

MEGA EMBARRASSMENT!

JET PROPULSION!

My pony Banjo and I were at our first affiliated jumping show and were really keen to get a clear round. As we cleared the first fence, Banjo let out a massive fart of jet propulsion! Banjo didn't just fart over the first jump though, he farted over every single jump, getting louder and louder until everyone could hear him. We did get a clear round but it's one of my most embarrassing memories, EVER!
Rosellen

EPIC EMBARRASSMENT!

MOUTHY MUCK

My ex-mate Natalie was not at all horsey, but she had asked to come and meet my pony, Candy. I was telling her all about ponies when Natalie did a huge yawn of boredom. Whilst her eyes were closed and her mouth was wide open, Candy squeezed out a parpy fart, straight into Natalie's mouth. She choked in disgust and then ran straight to the shops to buy some mints. Needless to say, she's still not forgiven me!
Anna

EPIC EMBARRASSMENT!

Got an embarrassing story to share? Share your cringe-worthy
moments with us by sending them to the usual PONY address or email

Make model pony storage jars!

This simple idea is easy, effective and a really cute way to keep stuff organised!

You will need

Plastic or glass jars with lids
Model ponies

Metallic spray
Paint

Glue
Glitter

How to do it!

1 Make sure your models, jars and lids are clean and 100% dry. Glue your model ponies to the lids and leave them to set.

Storage jars

You can use any type and size of jar, depending on what you want to store. We used an old jam jar and a large mayonnaise jar. Clean the jars thoroughly and soak them in hot water to remove the labels, using wire wool to scrub if necessary.

Model ponies

Small, lightweight plastic models will work best, preferably without hair for their mane and tail.

2 Now it's time to get creative! We sprayed one of our lids with silver metallic spray – we think he looks like a trophy!

Our other lid we painted purple (acrylic paint works best). We let it dry then painted it again with glue and gave it a dusting of glitter!

What to do with your jars

We are using our jars at PONY HQ for sweets, natch! But you can store absolutely anything in yours. Here are some ideas:

- Pony treats
- Plaiting bands
- Jewellery
- Loose change
- Beads and buttons

You are what you eat!

Good for you, good for him!

Lots of foods that are nutritionally good for you are also great for ponies. We may look different from the outside but inside, humans and horses are very similar. Our bones, organs, skin and body tissue all need the same nutrients in order to be healthy and to function well.

We all know that fruit and vegetables are good for us – not only are they low in fat and cholesterol, they are also high in fibre, meaning they are great for the digestive system. Here are a few healthy snacks, most of which (when eaten raw) you and your fave pony can share at the yard!

Carrots

Carrots are a real super food! They offer a good source of niacin (for healthy circulation and nervous system), manganese and vitamin A (great for the immune system), vitamin C (important for cell regeneration and healing) and vitamin K (for healthy blood and bones).

Apples

An apple a day keeps the doctor away! Apples are a good source of vitamin C and soluble fibre.

Watermelon

This is also a good source of potassium (an electrolyte which supports healthy muscle and nerve function) and a very good source of vitamin A and vitamin C. Ponies can eat the rind, which they enjoy as much, if not more, than the flesh! Ideally, remove the seeds as these can be difficult for ponies to digest.

Bananas

Bananas offer plenty of potassium and magnesium, as well as being a very good source of vitamin B6. In Australia, they feed ponies bananas like we feed carrots! Remember to remove the skins first though.

Beets – swede, turnip, parsnip

Beets are a good source of vitamin B6, folate, calcium, potassium and copper, vitamin C and manganese. Why not try hanging a swede or turnip in your pony's stable for him to eat and play with?

Celery

Riboflavin, vitamin B6, pantothenic acid, calcium, magnesium and phosphorus, vitamin A, vitamin C, vitamin K, folate, potassium and manganese – it's all in celery!

Pears

Pears are an extraordinary source of dietary fibre when the skin is eaten along with the flesh. Pears are also an excellent source of vitamin C and vitamin E, both powerful antioxidants and essential nutrients.

Cherries

Cherries are high in vitamin C. Make sure the stones are removed as these are poisonous.

Peaches, nectarines and mangoes

All these soft fruits make a sweet treat for your horse or pony, all are high in fibre – but be careful to remove all stones.

Some things to avoid...

❋ Greens such as broccoli, sprouts, peas and cauliflower are all packed full of vitamins but they aren't ideal for ponies as they can produce gasses which might lead to colic. So best to steer clear of these.
ALSO: ❋ Onions ❋ Rhubarb ❋ Tomatoes ❋ Avocado ❋ Potatoes

The rules of treating!

❋ *Be sure to remove any pips, stones or seeds from fruit*
❋ *Make sure anything you feed is always fresh!*
❋ *Only feed a small amount of fruit or veg at a time and remember that new food stuffs should be introduced to ponies' diets gradually*
❋ *Don't overfeed treats as it can encourage nippy behaviour in some ponies*

SPRING

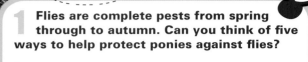

1 Flies are complete pests from spring through to autumn. Can you think of five ways to help protect ponies against flies?

1 _____
2 _____
3 _____
4 _____
5 _____

2 What is the name of the condition that causes itching and great discomfort, mainly around the mane and tail?

_____

3 What's the name of the midge that causes the itching?

_____

4 Explain why ponies have such a reaction to this midge:

_____

5 Laminitis is a painful condition of the hooves. When blood flow to the hooves is disrupted the sensitive, internal structure becomes inflamed and very painful. If oxygen to the area is starved for too long the bone in the hoof can move and rotate. What is this bone called?

_____

6 Can you identify three symptoms of laminitis?

1 _____
2 _____
3 _____

7 Ponies should never be starved, even laminitic ones. The best way to avoid laminitis is to keep them slim and trim. Name three ways of doing this:

_____
_____
_____

SUMMER

Pony

8 There are lots of plants that are poisonous to ponies but one yellow plant is particularly prevalent in fields across the countryside. What is it?

_____

9 What is the safest way to rid your fields of this plant?

_____

10 What do ponies with pink skin (especially on their muzzle) need extra protection against?

_____

11 Dehydration can be a problem at any time of year, but particularly during summer months. How much water should a pony drink a day?

_____

12 When grazing becomes less abundant ponies may start to scavenge hedgerows and trees for food. The nuts of which two trees are particularly poisonous to ponies and should be fenced off?

_____

AUTUMN

13 What condition can ponies develop when grazing on bare fields with sandy soil?

_____

14 What is this and why is it dangerous?

_____
_____
_____

How much do you know about seasonal disorders that affect our equine chums? Try our quiz and you'll soon find out!

vatch!

WINTER

15 What is the name of the common skin condition that develops when bacteria in the soil enters the skin?

_____

16 What areas on the pony are most commonly affected?

_____

18 They may be built to live outside but ponies still feel the cold. What is the best and most natural way to help ponies stay warm in the cold, winter month?

_____
_____
_____

17 The same bacteria can cause crusty scabs and lesions across the back on ponies that are turned out in winter without rugs. What is this skin disease known as?

_____

What's your score? Check the answers on page 98!

77

Charlie goes to a 1D concert!

CHARLIE LOOK, ONE DIRECTION ARE PLAYING JUST ROUND THE CORNER FROM US!

AND YOUR POINT IS...?

OH COME ON CHARLIE, I ALWAYS DO STUFF YOU WANT TO DO!

OH FINE I'LL COME. WHO ARE THEY ANYWAY?

COME ON CHARLIE, AS IF YOU DON'T KNOW.

I REALLY DON'T!

I'M SO EXCITED I COULD SCREAM!

DO YOU THINK I COULD DO MY HAIR LIKE HARRY?

YOU SAID YOU DIDN'T KNOW WHO THEY ARE!

WELL THEY'RE ALWAYS ON TV, AREN'T THEY?!

LET'S GET T-SHIRTS!

REALLY? OKAY!

CHARLIE, ARE YOU OKAY?

I MIGHT HAVE LIED A BIT - I'M A MASSIVE 1D FAN!

OMG IT'S THEM. CHARL, IT'S REALLY THEM!

WELL WHO ON EARTH WERE YOU EXPECTING?!

YOU DON'T KNOW, OH OH, YOU DON'T KNOW YOU'RE BEAUTIFUL!

I CAN'T SEE!

DUDE, SERIOUS!

THAT WAS AMAZING!

YEAH IT WAS. I HAD NO IDEA YOU WERE A FAN.

SIGNINGS? YES!!!

CHARLIE, WAIT!

signing tent

HARRY! WHAT HAIR PRODUCTS DO YOU USE?

UGGHHHH. HE IS LIKE, SOOO EMBARRASSING!

almost killed my friend's pony

When Kelly looked after her friend's pony, she didn't realise how easy it was for it to all go wrong...

"Would you like to look after Ditto when I'm on holiday?" asked my friend Lisa.

I was overjoyed – a pony of my own for a whole week. It was a dream come true for pony-mad, pony-less me.

"You know he's kept at part-livery, so you won't have to do much. He's mucked out and fed," my friend told me, "you'll just have to groom, ride him and clean his tack. Oh, and check on his water bucket throughout the day, if you can, because he drinks a lot."

Heaven!

A PONY OF MY OWN

Lisa went on holiday on Saturday and I couldn't wait to go to the stables and ride Ditto. I'm not as experienced as Lisa, but I could take Ditto on one of the riding school hacks, so that was okay. I was a bit disappointed not to have to look after him completely – I'd liked to have practised my pony care skills – but I wasn't complaining!

Ditto is a beautiful chestnut gelding, about 13.2hh and just gorgeous. I groomed him thoroughly, determined to show the riding school I was up to the task of looking after him. Then we went on a hack! I cleaned his tack when we returned, and asked whether I could give Ditto his feed, which he wolfed down. I hung around a bit, but then, eventually, I had to go home. Being a pony-owner, even by proxy, was great!

THIRSTY DITTO

Sunday and Monday passed in the same way. Grooming, riding, tack cleaning and feeding Ditto at lunchtime. On Tuesday we went for a hack and then I rode Ditto in my lesson in the school. When I got back to the yard the staff were already feeding the ponies and Ditto's feed was in his manger. I had a real struggle getting his bridle off – he wanted to eat his feed – but managed it eventually. Ditto's water bucket was empty, so I dutifully filled it and watched as Ditto took a long, grateful drink, dribbling water all over the floor as he went to look out over the door.

IT ALL STARTS GOING WRONG

As I finished cleaning the saddle I heard a scraping sound coming from Ditto's stable and, looking over his door, saw him pawing the ground. He had patches of sweat all over his body and he looked around at his belly and lifted a hind leg up, as if to kick himself.

"What's the matter, boy?" I said, not very worried.

"What's up?" asked Moira, one of the grooms at the school. "Oh no! Quick Kelly, run and get Mrs Bridge, Ditto's got colic!"

My blood ran cold. Colic? Why? How? I dashed to the house to tell Mrs Bridge, the owner of the school, and she followed me back, looking worried. She took one look at poor Ditto and called the vet on her mobile, telling him it was urgent and asking him to get to the yard as soon as possible.

"Kelly," she asked, carefully, "did you feed Ditto anything out of the ordinary?"

I shook my head. "No, nothing. He just had his feed then drank some water I put in for him," I told her.

Mrs Bridge caught her breath. "Don't you know that ponies shouldn't take a long drink of water after a feed?" she asked. "That's why Ditto's got colic!"

I ALMOST KILLED DITTO

Ditto pulled through – thank goodness. How could I have faced Lisa if he hadn't? How could I tell her that I had killed her pony? Luckily I didn't have to, but I had to tell her that I *almost* did. She was actually very understanding under the circumstances – but she never asked me to look after her pony again. And I can't say that I blame her.

> Ditto's water bucket was empty, so I dutifully filled it

> She took one look at poor Ditto and called the vet on her mobile

Ditto is a beautiful chestnut gelding

posed by models

Breed File!
American Cream Drafts

American Cream Drafts might be rare, but they are absolutely gorgeous! Read on to find out all about this stunning heavy horse!

Fab fact!
You can also get American White Drafts which are similar but are completely white with a white mane and tail!

The American Cream Draft is a rare breed developed in the USA. It is easily recognised by its cream colour which is known as gold champagne, although chestnuts can also occur. The Cream Draft's eyes are usually amber or hazel.

Fab fact!
American Cream Draft horses have pink skin so they can easily burn in the summer!

American Cream Drafts can also be a darker colour

History

The American Cream Draft was developed in the state of Iowa during the early 20th century. A cream mare called Old Granny was the foundation mare and most modern day American Cream Drafts can be traced back to her. She was foaled between 1900 and 1905, and was bought at an auction in Iowa in 1911 by Harry Lakin, a well-known stock dealer. He sold her to the Nelsons who bred a number of foals from her and so the breed was kick-started!

In the 1930s the Great Depression threatened to wipe out the American Cream Draft's existence, but breeders worked together to form a breed registry in 1944. The purpose of the breed registry was to improve the colour and breed type. Although the numbers of American Cream Drafts have increased the breed is still considered critical by the American Livestock Breeds Conservancy and the Equus Survival Trust. There are fewer than 2,000 American Cream Draft horses in the world!

The foals are very pale cream when born

Want to know more? If you'd like to find out more about this amazing breed check out the American Cream Draft Horse Association at www.acdha.org

Breed type and temperament

American Cream Drafts have refined heads, wide chests, sloping shoulders and short, strong backs. They have well-muscled hindquarters and are sure-footed with strong hooves. Mares are usually 15-16hh and stallions stand at 16-16.3hh.

Temperament-wise they are calm and willing, ideal for first time draft horse owners.

This blue-eyed foal is gorgeous!

FAB FACT!
American Cream Draft foals have blue eyes at birth, which then darken as they age!

Famous ones

The American Cream Draft horses that live in Colonial Williamsburg are known as the most famous American Cream Drafts. The horses are used to provide carriage rides through the village and a breeding programme aims to increase breed numbers.

This Cream Draft stallion is stunning!

Pics: Betty Shapiro, American Cream Draft Association and Shutterstock

The Nightrider

by Anna Dualé, aged 15

There is a legend that years ago, a rider was born. Not just an ordinary rider, but the Nightrider. The Nightrider was a mystical being who rode a white winged horse, which is known as his Nighthorse. The purpose of the Nightrider is that one night, he and his Nighthorse will be reborn and rediscovered, and will search the skies for the Dark Rider, an evil force who pledged years ago to cause pain and misery to the world, along with his own black winged horse, the Nightmare. No-one knows when the Dark Rider will strike, but whenever he does, the new Nightrider and his Nighthorse will be ready. And they will be waiting...

* * * * * * * *

The cool breeze lifts my long blonde hair off my shoulders, and Smithy's black mane waves gently in the wind. As we plod through the forest, I hear the soft, rhythmic thuds of Smithy's hooves echoing through the trees. As we reach the edge of the forest and emerge into a clearing, I wrap my leg's further around Smithy's stomach.

"Come on Smithy. Let's go!"

With a sudden spurt, Smithy leaps forward into a gentle, rocking-horse canter as I sit to his movement without any trouble. His strides lengthen and suddenly we're galloping madly across a vast meadow, the wind whipping his mane into my face, my hair streaming out behind me. The coarse strands of his mane cut into the flesh of my hands, but I don't care. I wrap my legs tighter around Smithy, and urge him on faster. He is only too willing to oblige.

Stretching out, we're hurtling across the grass, the pounding of hoofbeats echoing around the clearing, ringing in my ears. Smithy's coat is a blur of brown and white as we run. We're going so fast and so swift that for a moment I lose myself in the movement and, for a second, forget that we're actually on the ground. In my mind, we're not galloping at all, but we're flying. We're sailing high above the clouds, looking down on the world. The stars are so close I feel we can almost touch them. The snow-capped mountains are like huge purple pyramids as we soar beside them, and I'm able to feel the cold snow falling on my warm fingers.

* * * * * * * *

Suddenly, a vision swims before my eyes. I'm in the meadow, but it's night. A stunning white horse stands tall in the long grass, head held high, with his nostrils flaring. His huge and powerful wings are tucked into his body, mirroring a bird. A long forelock conceals his coal black eyes and his mane cascades down his neck and shoulders like a silvery, rippling waterfall. He stands alone in the vast clearing, surrounded by the silhouettes of the trees from the forest around him. The grass is long and reaches up to his belly and it dances and waves in the gentle breeze. Rising in the starry sky, the pale moon casts its luminous beam upon the earth, illuminating the meadow with an eerie glow.

I stand alone watching the magnificent creature outstretch his wings and give them a shake, before delicately folding them back by his sides. Suddenly, the temperature drops and I'm shivering violently in my thin cotton clothing. A strong gust of wind blows, almost knocking me off my feet. The moon hides behind a blanket of clouds, causing the only remaining light to disappear.

As my eyes gradually adjust to the gloom, I feel a dark, sinister force lurk closer towards me. I see nothing, but I can feel its presence. By pure instinct I know that the winged horse is in danger. I want to warn him, to get him to fly away from this place. But a strange feeling overcomes me and I can't speak. I feel my throat lock as a strong force prevents me from crying out. I begin to cough as the powerful hand strengthens its grip. The winged horse hears my suffocating chokes and takes to the air without a second glance. His wings beat powerfully as he sails through the air, gliding effortlessly across the night sky. I watch him in despair until he finally disappears from my sight. Then everything fades to black...

* * * * * * * *

I open my eyes to see Smithy looking down at me with a bewildered expression on his face as I lie in a heap on the ground. I groan and manage to stand. I feel dizzy so I lean on Smithy's solid neck. When the earth eventually stops spinning I climb gently onto Smithy's back and wrap my hands in his mane. I urge him on into a canter where we fly across the meadow, back the way we came.

* * * * * * * *

> Whenever the Dark Rider strikes, the new Nightrider and his Nighthorse will be ready

I toss and turn as I sleep tonight. I hear whispers. They're calling to me. I can't make out what they're saying. I listen carefully to the voices in my dreams... *You are the Nightrider,* they whisper. I wake with a start and sit bolt upright in bed.

I am the Nightrider. I climb out of bed and creep down to the stables. Smithy peers over his stable door.

"We have to go," I tell him. He watches me with an inquisitive look in his eyes. I open the door and whisper to him to keep quiet. Once we're outside, I vault onto his broad back and urge him to canter. As we arrive at the beginning of the forest, I slow Smithy down to a walk. I sit there, thinking about how I am the Nightrider. And I realise that if I'm the Nightrider, then Smithy must be my Nighthorse.

As we reach the clearing, the moon materialises out from behind the grey clouds, revealing its pale face. The cold wind blows strongly here as there are no trees to shield us. It's with a sudden realisation that I recognise the familiar scene. This is the meadow in my dreams. We will battle the Dark Rider and his Nightmare here. We step out into the clearing, and I shiver violently. I feel completely vulnerable and exposed and I want to race back into the trees and hide. But I stand my ground and wait for the Dark Rider to show up.

* * * * * * * *

Hours go by and I still sit upon Smithy's back, waiting patiently for the Dark Rider to appear. Minutes pass, merging into an hour. I decide to go back.

"Come on Smithy. Let's go!" We turn. A black horse is glaring at us. But this isn't any ordinary black horse. Her body looks bony and skeletal, her mane and tail clouds of black vapour materialising from her neck and rump. Her eyes are red and filled with seething hatred and intense loathing. Her wings are black and look nothing close to feathery, but are rough and scaly like a dragon. Sitting on board the beast's back sits a dark, armoured being, grasping a razor-sharp sword in his hand.

Before I have a chance to react, Smithy rears up onto his hind legs and thrashes his front legs wildly in mid-air.

"Smithy, stop!" I cry, clinging onto his neck for dear life. Suddenly, time seems to stop. Everything freezes as a blinding white light engulfs the clearing and everything in it. I hold on tight, since Smithy is frozen as the light consumes us. After a while, the light dwindles and eventually disappears. I slowly open my eyes and am flabbergasted to see what we have become. Smithy is no longer a cobby, skewbald gelding, but a striking white-winged stallion with a flowing mane and tail, his feathery wings huge and powerful. He holds his head up high and regards the Dark Rider and his Nightmare with an eye of contempt. He is wearing silver armoured plates around his chest and shoulders. Longer plates dominate his legs whilst his head is protected by an armoured *Shaffron*.

I peer down at myself. My shabby cotton clothing has been replaced by silver armour also. I am wearing the full garb, all except for the helmet. In one hand, I am clasping a silver rapier with a large ruby on its handle as I hold onto my horse's golden reins with the other. Smithy wears no saddle or bridle, only reins for me to guide him with.

In a sudden movement Smithy rears high in the air and unfolds his mighty wings, taking off into the air, his legs a swift blur as he gallops through the sky. I hear the Nightmare's infuriated squeals, a hideous sound which chills me to the bone. In an instant I can feel that they're following us. I turn around, but they are too close.

The Nightmare bares her teeth at us, white froth gushing from her ugly mouth. I push Smithy on, willing for him to go faster. But he is already at his full speed and his golden reins are slick with sweat. I turn again and see the Nightmare edging closer to us, until she is but a hair's breadth away. Baring her teeth, she lashes out and sinks her teeth into Smithy's rump, puncturing his skin. With an angry squeal, Smithy kicks out but misses and loses his balance. The Nightmare barges into Smithy causing him to fall. I scream as we plummet to the ground, Smithy unable to fly as I am not on his back. Arms flailing,

I shriek in terror as the ground rushes up to meet me.

I land hard and the wind is knocked out of me. I struggle to breathe and for a moment I forget where I am and what has happened. Then I remember my Nighthorse and notice him lying on the ground.

"Smithy!" I cry. I rush up to him and kneel by his side. There is an assortment of deep gashes all over his body, staining his white coat red.

"Come on Smithy," I plead. "You have to get up." I grab the reins and pull but he is too heavy. He's given up. And now, so have I. Without my Nighthorse, I am nothing.

* * * * * * * *

I take Smithy's head in my hands and rest my forehead against his. I close my eyes and remember the special times we've had together. Suddenly, I feel a crackle of energy travel through me and pass through to Smithy. It ripples through his body and reaches his wounds, where the force instantly dissolves his sores and cleans the blood from his coat. The energy decreases and disappears. My eyes open and Smithy slowly gets to his feet. With a final effort, he stands upright with a grunt. I give him a brief hug and leap onto his back. We have no time to lose. We take off into the air where the Dark Rider is waiting.

With a rush of power, Smithy lifts onto his hind legs in mid-air and thrusts his wings forward towards the Dark Rider. The mighty force drives them back. Smithy is extremely shattered, so now it's up to me.

Taking my rapier, I hold it above my head, take aim and fling it at the Dark Rider. The blade shreds through him and his Nightmare as if they were made of paper and a bright, red light glares from the cracks in their bodies. I shield my eyes, then the light disappears. I see nothing. The Dark Rider and his Nightmare have vanished.

* * * * * * * *

Alone with Smithy we hunt the night skies in search of the Dark Rider. He may be gone for a while, but he will return again one day. In years to come, I will be reborn. But for as long as I live now, Smithy will be my Nighthorse, and forevermore, I will be known as the *Nightrider.*

> By pure instinct I know that the winged horse is in danger

> I hear the Nightmare's infuriated squeals, a hideous sound which chills me to the bone

Brill Drill!

Drill riding is great fun! All you need is a group of riders and ponies, and someone to shout out instructions. Why not ask whether you can do some drill riding on your next lesson?

How many riders do you need?

As few as four and the sky's the limit, within reason. Between six and eight is ideal as you need to get the entire ride along the long side of the school for a drill ride to work efficiently. You do need an even number of riders and ponies, however.

What's that then?

Drill riding is like a musical ride (but you don't need the music!). Originally used by mounted regiments in the army, it provides a great way for riders to learn to regulate their horses' paces and ride as a team!

Okay, what's next?

The two best riders need to be leading file and second file, as they will be the two leaders. They need to set a reasonable pace, but be able to adjust their pace to suit the rest of the ride. Any ponies which are likely to kick should go at the back.

Time to get cracking!

Ride around as a ride and perform a few basic movements, such as splitting up at C and making pairs at A, and turning across the school altogether, and staying on the same rein. Once you are happy doing these basic exercises, you are ready to try some more difficult ones.

On to the movements! Here are some to try. Remember, it is always best to have someone knowledgeable to call out the movements for you. And if your lesson or ride is brilliant, why not see whether your local Pony Club would like to enter the Pony Club Musical Ride competiton!

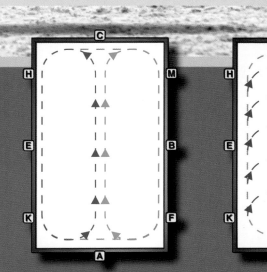

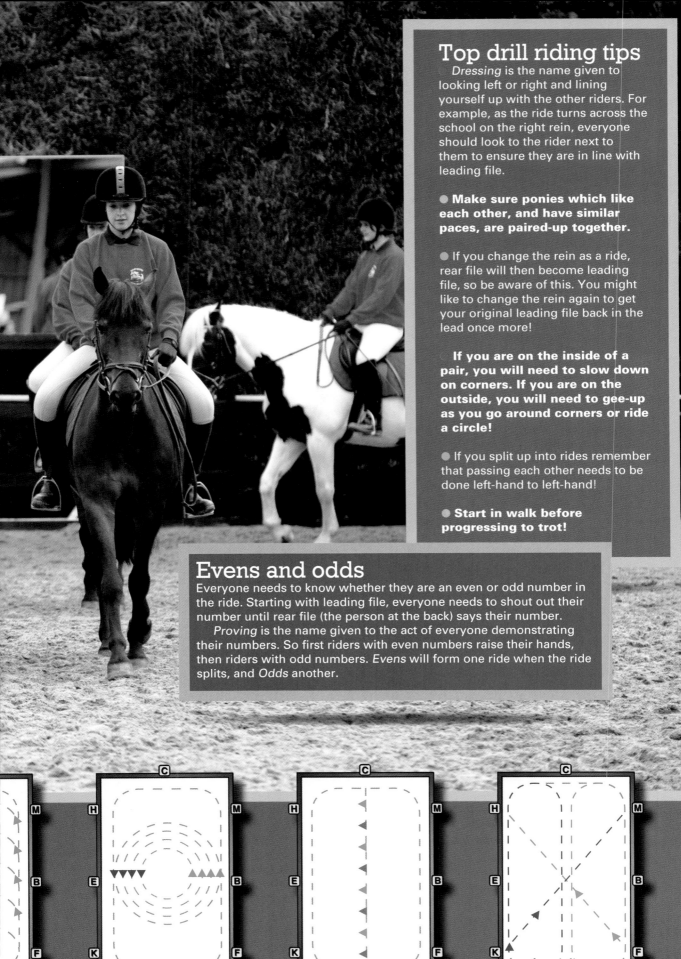

Top drill riding tips

Dressing is the name given to looking left or right and lining yourself up with the other riders. For example, as the ride turns across the school on the right rein, everyone should look to the rider next to them to ensure they are in line with leading file.

● **Make sure ponies which like each other, and have similar paces, are paired-up together.**

● If you change the rein as a ride, rear file will then become leading file, so be aware of this. You might like to change the rein again to get your original leading file back in the lead once more!

If you are on the inside of a pair, you will need to slow down on corners. If you are on the outside, you will need to gee-up as you go around corners or ride a circle!

● If you split up into rides remember that passing each other needs to be done left-hand to left-hand!

● **Start in walk before progressing to trot!**

Evens and odds

Everyone needs to know whether they are an even or odd number in the ride. Starting with leading file, everyone needs to shout out their number until rear file (the person at the back) says their number.

Proving is the name given to the act of everyone demonstrating their numbers. So first riders with even numbers raise their hands, then riders with odd numbers. *Evens* will form one ride when the ride splits, and *Odds* another.

ponymag.com is EPIC because...

tumblr.

Google+

Come and join the PONY community today

1 It is a one-stop fully interactive fun-filled pony-fest! Ponymag.com is a buzzing hive of activity where you can:

● Share your thoughts on every article, game and gallery!
● Share and like each post across all your favourite social media sites
● Read blogs from young riders and trainers

2 It's home to the PONY Shop! Featuring exclusive, bang-on trend products that you won't find anywhere else!

3 Mega competitions with loads of prizes to win, win, WIN!

4 It's also home to the PONY VIP Club secret area. This highly-exclusive zone contains special offers, secret links, games and tips from top riders. Wanna join the club? Visit ponymag.com to find out how!

5 There are tons of videos for riding and pony care, new issue chat from Penny and Duggie, plus anything that's fun, cute, crazy and horsey!

6 We have the most awesome, most addictive pony games on the planet! Play them for FREE and tell the other PONY gamers how well you did in the comment box underneath!

I'm the only boy at my yard!

Tom was unprepared for all the unwanted attention he got when he moved his pony to another stables!

I started riding because my mum has a horse. When I was tiny she would take me to the stables and leave me with the stable staff while she rode, but when I showed a liking for being led around on her big bay mare, Molly, she got me a pony. I was a typical boy rider, always getting Sunshine to canter when Mum was trotting, and urging her over logs in the woods, until I outgrew her and we got a smart 14.2hh dun gelding called Max.

Max likes going fast as much as I do, and we got used to riding out with Mum or on our own. But then the stables shut down and Mum and I had to move Molly and Max to another yard. Our last livery yard was a small place, with only seven other horses and all the other riders were grown ups. Our new yard had stabling for over 40 horses, and it was full up.

Full up with girls!

> I could feel myself going red. I didn't want to be a big hit with the girls

GIRLS UNLIMITED!

When I unloaded Max from the horsebox a large crowd of girls gathered around to see the new arrivals. I didn't realise they were looking at me as much as they were clocking Max! Mum gave me a knowing look:

"Looks like you're a big hit with the girls, Tom," she said, grinning.

I could feel myself going red. I didn't want to be a big hit with the girls. I just wanted to look after and ride Max. But as soon as I led him to his new stable one of the girls sidled up to me and gave me a dazzling smile.

"Hi, I'm Lauren," she said. "What's your name?"

I told her.

"We *must* go riding together," she said, flicking back her long, blond hair. Then two other girls arrived and introduced themselves. They said we should all go riding together, too.

"I don't think so," I managed to say, feeling all tongue-tied. "I'm used to schooling and riding Max alone, thanks."

CLINGY GIRLS

To cut a long story short, they wouldn't leave me alone. Every time I went to the stables to look after and ride Max, one or more of the girls would appear and hang around, offering to look after Max if I couldn't get to the yard, and asking when I was going riding so they could come with me. They were a nightmare. They didn't seem to understand that I didn't want to go riding with a load a girls, especially pushy ones like them!

It got to a stage where I dreaded going to see Max,

and he started to pick up on my angst, getting nervous and twitchy. It all came to a head when I made an excuse not to go to the yard with Mum twice in one week. Totally unusual!

"What's the matter, Tom?" she asked me, full of concern. "You're not going off riding Max, are you?"

I might have known I couldn't keep it from her – I told her how I hated the girls all jostling around me, never leaving me and Max alone.

"I'd like them a lot more if they'd just back-off a bit!" I said. "They're just so full-on and a pain!"

"Have you told them that?" asked Mum. I hadn't, of course, I'd felt far too intimidated by them. They were all so confident and they made me feel awkward and clumsy whenever they were around.

"Just tell them you want to be on your own," said Mum. "Be a bit more assertive, Tom. Don't let the girls get the better of you!"

> They were all so confident and they made me feel awkward and clumsy

THINGS GET BETTER

So I was. I took a deep breath and screwed up all my courage and told the girls I wouldn't go riding with *any* of them, and that I would appreciate them leaving me and Max to ride alone. And guess what? They did! I was amazed. And do you know what? Once they'd backed-off and were less in my face, I actually started to like them more. And now I'm friends with almost all of them, and we do go riding together. Sometimes, but not *always*. I still like to go riding with my mum now and again, and sometimes Max and I like it to be just the two of us. Just like old times.

posed by models

"Hi, I'm Lauren," she said.

87

PONY Puzzles!

Who am I?

Can you work out who these British Native ponies are from their brief descriptions?

1 I'm small, Scottish and can be a bit cheeky!
_____

2 I am a pony of four sections!
_____

3 My breed has mealy markings. In fact – we all look pretty similar!
_____

4 I am most often black and I hail from the north side of the Pennines.
_____

5 Also often black, but larger than number 4, I hail from the east side of the Pennines!
_____

6 I am Ireland's pony breed and an ace jumping pony.
_____

7 I am an ancient breed and often display primitive markings on my back and legs.
_____

8 I'm a Hampshire pony born-and-bred, and you can still see me living feral in the forest!
_____

9 I am a quality riding pony from south Devon.
_____

Spot the difference

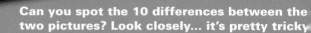

Can you spot the 10 differences between the two pictures? Look closely... it's pretty tricky

Grooming kit jumble

Can you count the number of body brushes, dandy brushes and plastic curry combs in the jumbled up mess of kit?

Body brushes

Dandy brushes

Hoof pick

Sweat scraper

Hunt the apple tree!

One of the trees in this field is laden with apples but can you work out which one it is? Start at square A1 and follow the instructions to find the apples!

| | A | B | C | D | E | F | G | H | I | J | K | L | M | N | O | P | Q |

Instructions

Answers to all the puzzles can be found on p98!

1 Go south seven squares

2 Go east two squares

3 Go north three squares

4 Go north-east two squares

5 Go south-east one square

6 Go south six squares

7 Go north-east three squares

8 Go north-west one square

9 Go north four squares

10 Go east four squares

11 Go south-west one square

12 Go south-east one square

13 Go south two squares

14 Go east three squares

15 Go south two squares

16 Go south-west one square

17 Go west four squares

18 Go north two squares

19 Go east one square

The apple tree is at square

89

Part 2

Duggie's Dreams!

PAINTED PONIES!

Native American Indians used ponies for hunting and in war, as well as for transport. But why did they paint symbols on their war ponies? Read on to find out more!

WAR PONIES

The Native American Indians were introduced to horses in the 1600s by Spanish Conquistadores and, very quickly, the horse became a natural part of their lives. Horses which escaped the Spanish evolved into tough, pony-like Mustangs. Horses enabled the Native American Indians to hunt bison and to travel across the land, but they were also used in war. Using horses in battle enabled the Native American Indians to fight against those who tried to oppress them.

WHY PAINT?

Painting their ponies was a way to show off achievements, as well as to harness the power of the spirits and gods. Each symbol had an individual meaning, as shown on this image! Cool, huh? All the paints were made from the natural resources available such as bark, moss, clay and blood.

FAB FACT!

The majority of Native American Indians owned Appaloosas or Paint horses because they were sure-footed, strong, fast and blended into the scenery

COLOUR CO-ORDINATION

Different colours also had different meanings. Red symbolised war, blood, strength, energy and power. Black was used to symbolize victory. White was for peace, while blue symbolised wisdom and confidence. Yellow was the colour of death and indicated that the rider and pony were brave and willing to fight to the death. Green was the symbol of endurance, but it was also believed to improve vision. Lastly, purple symbolised power, mystery and magic!

EYE CIRCLE	Improve the pony's vision
NOSTRIL CIRCLE	Improve the pony's sense of smell
THUNDER STRIPES	On the front legs to add power and speed and to please the God of War
ARROWHEADS	Painted on all four hooves to make the pony swift and nimble-footed
FIRE ARROW	To cause the enemy trouble and give strength to the Indian warrior
HANDPRINTS	On the chest to show how many enemies he had knocked down
HAIL STONES	A prayer that hail stones would fall on the enemy
RED HANDPRINT	Also known as the Pat Hand Print, this symbol was a sign that the pony had brought his rider home unharmed from a dangerous battle

The Native American Indian would also weave a medicine bag onto his pony's bridle, which contained special items belonging to him or items thought to hold supernatural powers. No one, apart from the owner, was allowed to look inside the bag and if the owner died it was buried with him. Feathers were also braided into the forelock and tail because they were a symbol of power.

GIVE IT A GO!

Why not paint your pony with some Native American Indian symbols? You could even devise your own symbols with your pony mates and come up with a code!

2014 – bring it on!

Discover what 2014 has in store for you, according to the stars!

Aquarius
January 21 – February 19

2014 will be a busy year, but it could be brilliant, too! You may find yourself thinking deeply about your riding, but make sure this is in a positive way. You may have to stop yourself thinking negative thoughts – you're a better rider than you think!

The riding skills you are concentrating on now will last you a lifetime, so don't worry that you are wasting your time. Focus on fun and relationships in the second half of the year.

Pisces
February 20 – March 20

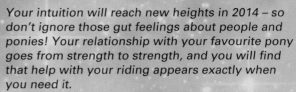

Your intuition will reach new heights in 2014 – so don't ignore those gut feelings about people and ponies! Your relationship with your favourite pony goes from strength to strength, and you will find that help with your riding appears exactly when you need it.

Don't worry if you feel some of your hard work goes unnoticed. Important people can see how hard you work, and appreciate your worth.

Aries
March 21 – April 20

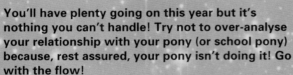

You'll have plenty going on this year but it's nothing you can't handle! Try not to over-analyse your relationship with your pony (or school pony) because, rest assured, your pony isn't doing it! Go with the flow!

You may be considering a career with horses – do your research to ensure this is really what you want. You may need to balance your money as far as buying all your pony needs, or saving for riding lessons. Prioritise!

Taurus
April 21 – May 21

If you have worries over your pony or riding, sharing these with a good friend will help. You could feel some insecurity in 2014 – maybe things are changing at the yard, or you are outgrowing your pony – but don't worry. Stay organised and take things one at a time.

Volunteering to help others figures in your chart this year – maybe at the Pony Club, with charity work or at the RDA. Autumn is a time for fun, so get out there and enjoy your riding!

Gemini
May 22 – June 21

A peculiar mix of emotions and learning figures in your chart in 2014. Try not to get upset in lessons, and take all advice on the chin to take your riding to greater heights. Networking and socialising are also highlighted, so make the most of friendships, and make new ones – perhaps new people at your yard or Pony Club.

2014 is the year when you are able to get totally focused on what you really want from your riding. Remember your goal and go for it!

Cancer
June 22 – July 22

2014 is the year for you to let your hair down! Inject some fun into your riding instead of concentrating on schooling, schooling, schooling. Remember that a balance between hard work and fun is essential to keep you and your fave pony happy and inspired.

You could have more responsibilities this year – maybe someone wants you to help with their pony. Working hard will reap rewards in this area.

Leo

July 23 – August 23

You're feeling restricted at the moment, but paying attention to your situation at the yard or riding school will make these feelings disappear.

You could feel rather possessive this year – maybe someone else decides your fave riding school pony is their fave, too, or your pony gets a little too friendly with some of your friends, but you can overcome this.

People recognise your natural riding talent, so you can understand how you are valued.

Virgo

August 24 – September 22

2014 could be an adventurous year for you and feelings of wonderlust fuel the desire to break out and do something more daring. Maybe it's time to try something new, riding-wise, or push for a riding holiday.

Your relationship with your pony or riding school pony goes from strength-to-strength – but remember to reward him or her for extra effort you may ask for.

Libra

September 23 – October 22

You should enjoy a year where your riding and horse knowledge increase beyond your wildest dreams – providing you are prepared to work to achieve this. This hard work will mean you will gain great satisfaction from achieving your goals.

From April to November you should find that your relationship with your pony is particularly strong. You are a team to be reckoned with!

Scorpio

October 23 – November 21

Have you started a horsey project? If so, you could benefit from this during the latter part of 2014. You are working hard with regard to your riding and pony knowledge, but remember to factor some time for something lighter – a gymkhana, a picnic ride, hacking out with friends, perhaps – to chill out and relax.

Make sure both you and your pony eat healthily to get the most out of the year.

Sagittarius

November 22 – December 21

You hate routine, and 2014 may be the year when some of you decide to change certain areas of your life. Maybe it's time to make new riding friends, or progress to another pony – or even change yards!

New friends could be good for you this year, and make sure they give you the freedom you crave – without making them feel you do not value their friendship. This is also true with the ponies you ride – don't forget their feelings.

Capricorn

December 22 – January 20

You could be making big changes in your pony's living accommodation in 2014. Maybe a stable makeover is in order.

Don't worry if you do not have so many friends in 2014, because the ones you do have, are true ones. This reinforces your need to be a little more private in your thinking and riding. You know what projects you want to work on, and are not in the mood to be swept along by others who may have their own agendas.

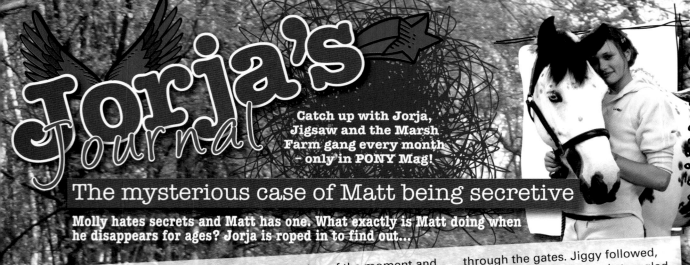

Jorja's Journal

Catch up with Jorja, Jigsaw and the Marsh Farm gang every month – only in PONY Mag!

The mysterious case of Matt being secretive

Molly hates secrets and Matt has one. What exactly is Matt doing when he disappears for ages? Jorja is roped in to find out...

It was Molly who first noticed. I'm always wandering around with my head in the clouds. It's Molly who's the sharp one. It's Molly who notices things.

"Matt's going for very long rides these days," she said, as Matt rode his chestnut pony CP out of the Marsh Farm gates and headed off along the bridlepath.

"Hmmmm," I said, dividing Jigsaw's forelock into three. I was practising different ways of plaiting it and not getting very far. To be honest, I wasn't really interested in where Matt was going but what Molly said next changed my mind.

"I reckon he's got another girlfriend," she said, her eyes narrowing, her lips pursed together. I could practically hear her brain whirling as I digested this idea. I still thought of Matt and Angelina as an item, even though they hadn't been seeing each other for over a year. Angelina was seeing someone else, so why shouldn't Matt?

"Do you really think so?" I asked, following her gaze just in time to see CP's flaxen tail disappear into the gloom of the trees.

We ought to follow him!" said Molly, her eyes gleaming.

My heart sank. I recognised the decisive tone to Molly's voice and the last thing I felt like doing was haring around the countryside on a wild goose – or Matt chase.

"Come on, let's saddle up pronto!" demanded my friend.

Jigsaw gave me a surprised look as I hurried to saddle up and put her bridle on. Then, before either Jigsaw or I could say *wait for us*, we were off behind Molly and her pony Star, trotting along the bridlepath looking for Matt. We didn't find him. The trail, as they say, was cold. Freezing. Ice age.

"Manure heaps!" said Molly, as we reached a fork in the path and didn't know which way to go. It was

her expression of the moment and didn't go down too well at school.

"Oh come on," I said, trying not to yawn, "let's just go for a nice ride." I reminded myself of my gran whose answer to everything is to have what she calls a '*nice cup of tea.*' I made a mental note not to use the word *nice* in future, on the basis that it makes me sound about 75. Which I don't particularly want.

So we did. Go for a nice ride, that is, not have a nice cup of tea (as if!). And when we got back Matt was still out. He hadn't returned by the time we had turned out the ponies, cleaned tack (okay, only Molly cleaned tack, I sat and watched), and headed for home.

It was a bit odd. Molly was definitely on to something and Matt was definitely up to something, which made me definitely in the middle of two somethings!

Three days later, Molly rushed up to Jigsaw's stable, thrust her head over the half-door like Jigsaw does

> "Manure heaps!" said Molly, as we reached a fork in the path and didn't know where to go.

when she sees me approaching with her feed bucket and hissed, "Quick, saddle up, Matt's going for a ride!"

"Oh no, not again!" I groaned. But Molly was gone, throwing her tack on Star and causing him to back into his water bucket and snort like a dragon.

We were in the saddle in record time. Then we realised that we'd beaten Matt to it – he was still in the tack room.

"Now what?" I asked. "You can't follow someone when you're in front of them!"

"We'll hide in the woods," said Molly, undaunted, heading Star out

through the gates. Jiggy followed, snatching at the grass as I struggled to tighten her girth. I know you're supposed to do it with one hand when you're mounted but I always have to enlist the help of my other hand to haul on the girth, which means I have zero control over Jiggy, which she thinks is funny!

Only Matt didn't pass us. We waited for ages, Jiggy's mouth and bit turned green with all the grass I let her eat and Star went into meltdown when some rubbish blew under his nose, but there was no sign of Matt. There was, however, another rider who pulled up and gave us a strange look.

"Whatever are you two doing?" We knew that voice. Devon, the yard's dressage diva, on her pony Raven, both looking at us in that supercilious way only Devon and Raven have perfected.

"Nothing!" exclaimed Molly, sounding totally guilty.

"You two are always up to something," Devon sighed, turning Raven in a dressage-y way, sort of pirouetting on the spot until she faced the opposite way. I was wildly jealous and decided I'd teach Jiggy to do it. Only one problem: I don't know *how* to do it. I wondered whether I could find it on the internet or something.

As Devon and Raven walked off, Molly and I exchanged glances. Some spies we were!

"I'm not leaving the yard tonight until Matt's back," declared Molly.

"Why are you so bothered?" I asked her.

Molly narrowed her eyes. "I hate secrets," she replied.

We only just caught Matt coming back. He'd been gone for hours and hours and *hours.*

"He can't possibly have been riding all this time," hissed Molly, as we looked out from our hiding place in the tack room.

I nodded in agreement. But where had Matt been, and what had he been doing?

Three days later it rained. Molly was jubilant. "Come on," she said, "we can follow CP's hoofprints."

So we did. We followed them to the common, over the common, past the common and on towards the park. We followed them around the park, towards the huge hedges and bushes which skirted the golf course. Then the hoofprints stopped.

> "Perhaps CP has learned to fly," I suggested. "Like Pegasus!"

Just like that. We looked at each other in puzzlement.

"Perhaps CP has learned to fly," I suggested, mildly bored and not very curious. "Like Pegasus."

"No, Matt turned off the path," replied Molly, as though my suggestion had been a serious one. "Look, you can see where CP has pushed through the bushes. Come on, we'll follow!"

We pushed our way through, too, getting thoroughly soaked by the leaves. Jiggy must have got some water in her ear because when we did finally get to the other side of the hedge she threw her head around, then rubbed her ear on her knee, almost pulling me out of the saddle.

"Oh Molly, this is so not fun!" I moaned. I was aware that I was becoming very negative and decided I had to watch it. I was doing nothing but moan. Not good.

Suddenly we heard a neigh – and Jigsaw neighed back.

"Shhhhh!" hissed Molly. "You'll give us away!"

"How exactly am I supposed to stop her?" I asked. I don't know whether you've ever been on a pony when they neigh, but their rib cage vibrates and I felt all rattled. In more ways than one!

Creeping forward we discovered CP, nibbling grass, his stirrups run up, girth loosened, bridle hanging on a nearby branch.

"Why is he tied up here?" I asked. We were in the middle of nowhere.

"At least Matt has replaced his bridle with a headcollar," said Molly, a stickler for correct horse management.

Of Matt there was no sign.

"Let's untie CP and take him home!" said Molly, leaning over to work on the quick-release knot.

"You can't!" I protested. "Matt will freak out when he comes back!"

"Serves him right for being so horribly secretive!"

"It doesn't Molly. I'm having nothing to do with it. I'd be beside myself if I thought Jiggy had been stolen or wandered off."

"You're not Matt!"

"You know he loves CP! I'm going to find him and tell him what you're up to!"

Molly stopped untying CP and looked all sulky. "Okay," she said. "But I bet I know what Matt's up to!"

"What?" I asked, not terribly bothered about it.

"I bet you any money you like that he's playing golf. We're right on the edge of the course."

"So?"

"Don't you see? Matt's tying up CP, sneaking in the back way and playing golf without paying! I bet he's got his golf clubs stashed away in the bushes somewhere, and that he picks them up, uses them and then hides them again."

"You don't know that!"

"No, but I bet you any money you like that..."

"Yeah, okay, I get it," I interrupted. "Why are you so bothered about it?"

Molly sat up taller in the saddle and looked at me with a shocked expression. "It's *stealing!*" she said, dramatically.

"Oh," I said. "I suppose it is. But I'm not going to tell on him, and neither, I hope, are you!" I felt quite protective of Matt. I know he and his mum don't have much money, and he struggles to keep CP. I also knew he loved playing golf and that it was very expensive and even though I don't agree with stealing, I didn't like the idea of Molly stirring things up for him. I was totally torn.

Molly just made a noise which sounded like *wmmmfff*, and went into a sulk. "Okay," she said, finally, "let's wait for him!" Her face was set and I knew it was impossible to argue with her. I decided I'd stick up for Matt when he did appear. I didn't have to agree with Molly.

We dismounted and loosened the ponies' girths, then we took off our riding hats and sat on a convenient fallen tree while I let Jiggy munch on some grass. Molly didn't want Star to graze with his bit in, but eventually she gave in – mainly because Star wore her down, almost pulling her off the tree trunk in an effort to get some grass. It did seem mean when both CP and Jiggy were

munching away.

We waited for ages. Then some more. Then ages, and ages more. Even Jigsaw got bored. Eventually, Matt emerged from the bushes, whistling. You should have seen his face when he saw us!

"What are you two doing here?" he asked, untying CP and giving him a pat while he replaced the headcollar with his bridle.

"Waiting for you," said Molly. "We know you've been playing golf without paying And that's *stealing!*" accused Molly.

"Hold on Molly, you don't know that, and besides," I said, "it's none of our business."

"That's where you're wrong," said Molly, playing her trump card. "My dad happens to be a member of this club, and he will be livid when I tell him."

Matt gave me a funny look. "Even so, Jorja's right, it isn't any of your business," he said, "but actually you're wrong, Molly. Totally, absolutely, completely wrong!"

"Oh," said Molly. Then she said nothing. Which was a first.

"What are you doing then?" I asked, curious.

"Caddying," Matt replied. "You know," he continued, seeing our

> "Let's untie CP and take him home!" said Molly, leaning over to work on the quick-release knot.

blank faces, "carrying a golfer's clubs around so he doesn't have to. I get paid. Money. Which I need for CP and to play golf. So there!"

"Oh," said Molly again.

I beamed at Matt, relieved he hadn't been doing anything dodgy. "I'm so glad," I said.

I have to hand it to Molly, when she's made a mistake she does the right thing. "I'm sorry, Matt," she said. "I was totally wrong about the situation and I misjudged you. Will you accept my apology?"

Matt winked at her. "Of course, you batty old thing. Honestly Molly, you're raving bonkers sometimes!"

We all rode home together – and Molly, keen to make up for her mistake, actually talked to Matt (instead of arguing, which she usually does) and by the time we got to the yard you could almost, *almost,* mistake them for friends.

I don't know how long it will last, but I'm making the most of it!

The Ans

Puzzles (pages 34-35)
Super sudoku

Giant wordsearch

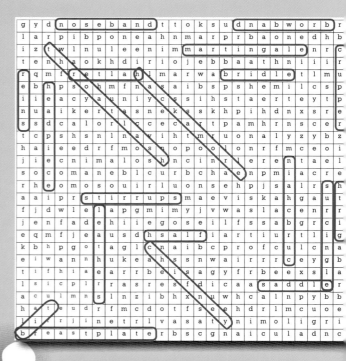

Unscramble the celebs

1. Francis Whittington
2. William Whitaker
3. Mary King
4. Carl Hester
5. Laura Collett
6. Georgie Spence
7. Jonathon Paget
8. Zara Phillips
9. Ellen Whitaker
10. Sophie Christiansen
11. Carl Hester
12. Oliver Townend
13. Charlotte Dujardin
14. Tina Cook
15. Tim Stockdale

Puzzles (pages 64-65)
Odd one out

1. Tim Stockdale
2. Stocking
3. Croup
4. Tail
5. Bareback
6. Milk
7. Dalmatian
8. BSP
9. Andalusian
10. Major

Perfect pairs

1. Racing silks
2. Mangalarga Marchador
3. Iron grey
4. Strawberry roan
5. Cleveland Bay
6. Show jumping
8. Freestyle dressage

Riddle 1

The rope isn't tied to anything, so the horse can go freely to anywhere it pleases.

Riddle 2

The youngest son rides on his brother's horse, knowing that his own horse is the slowest.

wers!

Here are the answers to all the PONY Puzzle pages, and some quizzes, too!

Point taken!

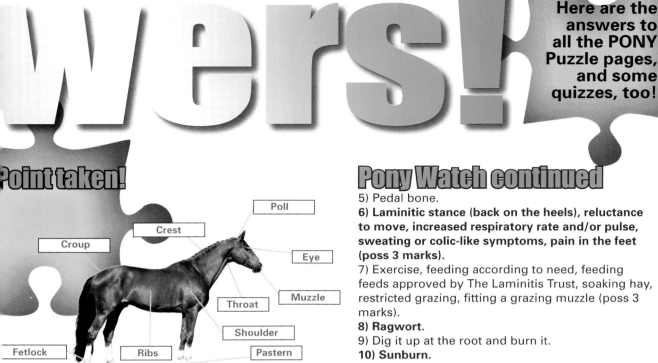

Poll
Crest
Croup
Eye
Muzzle
Throat
Shoulder
Fetlock
Ribs
Pastern
Coronet

Great gridwork

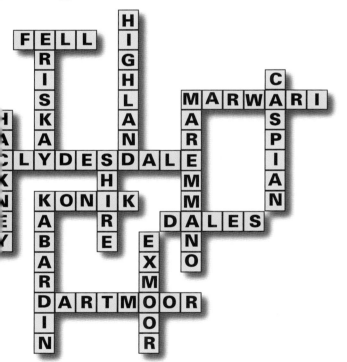

Pony Watch (pages 76-77)

) Fly repellent, fly mask/fringe, fly rug, field shelter/
hade, keep pony in at dusk and dawn, garlic/immunity
upplements, fly catching strips, collars and tags, poo pick
elds regularly and keep stables clean (poss 5 marks).
) **Sweet itch.**
) Culicoides midge.
) **When the midge bites it injects an anticoagulant
prevents the blood from clotting) which ponies are
llergic to.**

Pony Watch continued

5) Pedal bone.
6) **Laminitic stance (back on the heels), reluctance to move, increased respiratory rate and/or pulse, sweating or colic-like symptoms, pain in the feet (poss 3 marks).**
7) Exercise, feeding according to need, feeding feeds approved by The Laminitis Trust, soaking hay, restricted grazing, fitting a grazing muzzle (poss 3 marks).
8) **Ragwort.**
9) Dig it up at the root and burn it.
10) **Sunburn.**
11) 27-54 litres.
12) **Acorns and beech nuts (poss 2 marks).**
13) Sand colic.
14) **Build up of sand in the intestinal tract causes a blockage in the intestine, leading to colic.**
15) Mud fever.
16) **Heels and lower leg.**
17) Rainscald.
18) **Feed plenty of hay. As the pony digests fibre it replaces heat that helps keep them warm from the inside out.**

Puzzles (pages 88-89) Who am I?

1 = Shetland
2 = Welsh
3 = Exmoor
4 = Fell
5 = Dales
6 = Connemara
7 = Highland
8 = New Forest
9 = Dartmoor

Spot the difference

Candle stick, door handle, spots on sofa, glasses, girl's top, girl's tongue, Charlie's shirt, sofa legs, Charlene's eyes, Charlie beads of sweat!

Grooming kit jumble

Body brush - 6
Dandy brush - 6
Hoof pick - 7
Sweat scraper - 7

Find the apple tree

The apple tree is at K7.

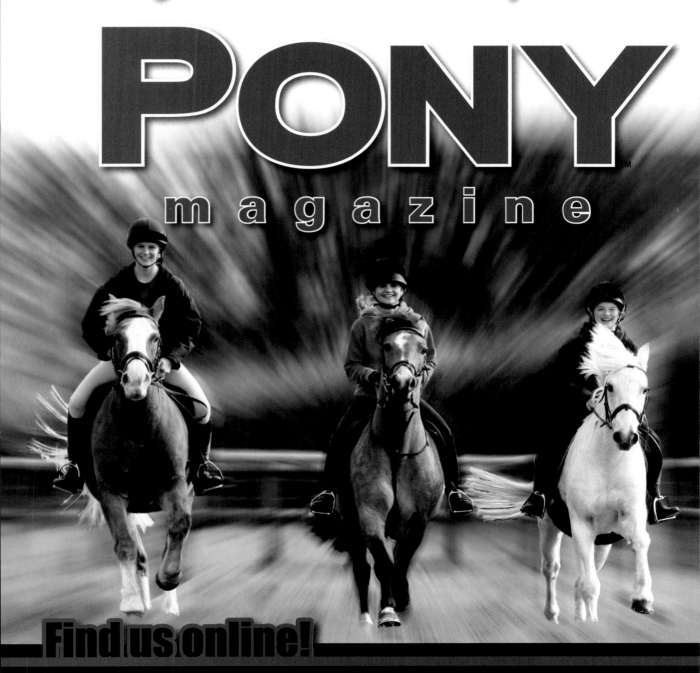

out of the saddle!